MASSEY-HARRIS-FERGUSON

of the founding of Massey Ferguson

1953-1958

MASSEY-HARRIS-FERGUSON

Memories

of the founding of Massey Ferguson

1953-1958

JOHN FARNWORTH

First Published 2007

ISBN: 978 1 904686 14 9

A catalogue record of this book is available from the
British Library

Published by

Japonica Press
Low Green Farm, Hutton, Driffield,
East Yorkshire, United Kingdom, YO25 9PX
www.classictractors.co.uk

Design and page layout by Banks Design

CONTENTS

Foreword   vi

Acknowledgements   vii

Preface   viii

Background   12

The Merger   24

Memories   58

Mr Ferguson's Personal Private Assistant (UK)   58
Mr Anthony Sheldon

A Quick Appointment (UK, USA)   60
Sir Ian Wallace

Looking After the Estate (UK)   64
Peter Warr

In India at the Time (India, UK)   66
John Armstrong

Workshop Projects and Scrapping Prototypes   (UK)   67
"Hammie" (Hamilton) T. Baird

Colourful Models, Rounded Designers and that Spanner (USA)   69
Donald G Bamford

Working Itself Out! (UK and New Zealand)   70
Keith Base

No Animosity (UK)   73
J R Bibby, Harry Ferguson's Prototype Testers' Foreman

Personal Assistant (UK, USA, Canada, USSR, China)   73
Len Boon

A Farm by the Factory (Scotland)   76
John Caldwell

Training at Stoneleigh (UK)   78
Bob Dickman

Testing the Ferguson Combine at the Time (USA)   81
Bob Doll

An Iowa Ferguson and Massey Dealer (USA)   85
Ted Feekes

Another Stoneleigh Instructor's Memories of the M-H-F Period (UK)   87
Colin Fraser

Confessions of a "Grey Man" (who became a red and grey!) (UK, Denmark)   89
Erik Fredriksen

The Birth of Stoneleigh Training School, then Onwards for 42 years (UK)   92
John Garlick

Field Testing the "Innovative" Baler and Forage Harvester (USA)   95
D.E. "Del" Gentner

"The Circus Comes to Town" (UK)   100
Bob Gilchrist

From Father to Son (Canada, New Zealand, Rhodesia)   110
Leeroy Gordon

My Hobby was my Job (USA)   112
Robert A Hadley

Farming with the LTX: a Lad's Recollections and Comparisons (UK)   116
Derek Hiatt

Put a Boy in the Baler Tool Box (UK)   118
Brian Johnson

Ferguson: Specialists and Organisation (Canada)   122
Harold Jonah

Experiencing the LTX Tractor – and More (UK)   123
Nigel Liney

South Africa Assignment – First Class and Armed! (South Africa)   128
Robin H Litton

The Origins of MF in South Africa
(South Africa)   130
J P A Maitre

The Oldest of Recollections (Canada)   133
"Purc" McMaster

Sent to Coventry (Scotland and England)   135
Alex McMillan

Evaluating the M-H 735 Combine (Scotland and UK)   138
Jim Mc Naught

On the Heavy Clay Lands (Canada)   139
Don Mc Vittie

Meanwhile, In Australia ...... (Australia)   140
(R.V.) Dick Muspratt

Engine Testing (UK)   145
Nibby Newbold

A Wealth of Information (N Ireland and UK)   147
Alex Patterson

"Service Pays All Ways" (England, Eire, Scotland, Wales, Italy, India)   154
Bill Percival

Improvisation in India (India)   158
David Perrott

Fergusons Sold and Remembered; and Ferguson stories! (Belgium, Germany, France)   160
Maurice Pol-Fraikin

Trouble-Shooting with Massey-Ferguson (USA)   164
Donald R Potter

From M-H to MF via M-H-F (Scotland, England, Algeria, Eire, Canada)   166
Bryan Rogers - May 1948

Take it in your Stride! (USA)   172
Don Snyder

Agricultural Engineer (UK)   173
Alan Starley

A few Memories (UK)   176
Colin Steventon

From Armaments to Industrials (USA)   176
Roy K Stuart

The oldest of Recollections (Italy, Egypt, Mali, Senegal, Sudan, Turkey, Iraq) 184
Charles Voss

Designing all the Way - M-H Kilmarnock to M-F Coventry (Scotland and England) 195
Jim Wallace

"Dogsbody" in Yugoslavia (Yugoslavia)   204
Bud White

Overview of how MF in the UK progressed in the
decade after Massey-Harris-Ferguson   206
Lance Parker

FOREWORD

In producing this book John Farnworth has made a notable contribution to the published records of the farm machinery industry and the experiences of some of the people connected with a significant period in its history. The merger of the Massey-Harris and Ferguson companies brought together one of the earliest pioneers of the industry and the company representing the greatest advance in tractor design. It also brought together their two leaders, James Duncan and Harry Ferguson, already well known to each other. As Massey-Harris was the senior partner, Mr Duncan became President of the new Massey-Harris-Ferguson organisation; another distinguished Canadian like so many of the Massey family before him.

John has already had eight books published on the Massey-Harris, Ferguson and Massey Ferguson companies and products. These include "Ferguson. The Hunday Experience" compiled jointly with John Moffitt who until recently held in his Hunday museum the most comprehensive collection of Ferguson equipment, and which was the subject of a major pageant in 1999.

The Hunday book, like this one, included some pieces by former employees. In his preface that follows John remarks that there is no better way to recall the atmosphere and events of the merger period. I am sure that readers will agree and that using them to produce a major book strengthens such an historical record.

I joined the Ferguson company as a trainee in 1950 after Naval service and university. The Ferguson Training Centre was then in the Stoneleigh Abbey old buildings, garages and stables, before moving to the Stoneleigh Deer Park. My first appointment was to the staff of Noel Newsome, Public Relations Manager, together with Tony Lees who had formerly edited the "Farmer and Stockbreeder" magazine. I was with them in London for the Press Conference announcing the merger.

Noel Newsome had been " The Man in the Street" with the BBC Overseas Service during the war. He and Tony did much to give substance and added publicity to Harry Ferguson's "Price Reducing System", his campaign which is well covered in the "Hunday" book.

Harry Ferguson was a visionary as well as a brilliant engineer and entrepreneur, a rare combination of these three attributes. I am sure that he was genuinely motivated by the desire that through advances in mechanisation world agriculture would produce sufficient food at prices that everyone could afford.

Jeremy Chance

Manager of the Massey-Ferguson Training Centre at Stoneleigh 1971-1974

ACKNOWLEDGEMENTS

M y very sincere thanks are due to all those who have contributed their memories and often photos to this book. Without them it would not have been possible to produce a book of this type. Special thanks go to George and Barb Smyth in Ontario who helped locate old M-H-F employees in Canada, and Paul Nelson, editor of the Ferguson Furrows magazine who similarly helped in the USA.

I owe a considerable debt of gratitude to the late Mr. L J (Len) Boon who started with Massey-Harris in Canada in 1948 and went on to hold a succession of posts in both Massey-Harris, Massey-Harris-Ferguson and Massey Ferguson, culminating in him being the Director of the Special Operations Division for Massey Ferguson. Len had an incredible knowledge of the workings of the company as it evolved from Massey-Harris to Massey Ferguson and he was intimately involved with the actual merger. Len always acted as Personal Assistant to James Duncan whenever he was in the UK or on missions to continental Europe. He was kind enough to indulge me in lengthy discussions and correspondence about post-war Massey-Harris, the merger and the development of the Special Operations Division. Through him I gained an astonishing feel of the workings of the companies in those now quite far-off

times. It is worth recalling here that it was Len who, after Harry Ferguson had lost the famous coin toss for 1,000,000 dollars, was assigned the task of having it mounted for later presentation to the gallant loser. I had thought about preparing such a book as this for quite a long time; it was Len Boon who gave me the inspiration to follow through with the idea.

Thanks are due to AGCO for permission to reproduce their advertising material and photos supplied through their audio visual department by Ted Everett and Ivor Clarke. Ted completed 50 years service with successively Ferguson, Massey Ferguson and then AGCO in 2002. Thanks also to John Kirkham in AGCO.

The University of Guelph Rural Heritage Centre allowed me access to their archives and thanks are due to Lynn Campbell who did the research for material.

For various help with photos, pieces of information and contacts (this has been absolutely vital!) I must especially thank John Bush, Jean Cherouvrier, Murray Ellis, Erik Fredriksen, Bob Gilchrist, David Harrowfield, Nigel Liney, David Lory, Paul Nelson, Jim Russell, Colin Steventon, Robert Voss, Jim Wallace, Ross Ward.

Finally thanks as always to my wife Moira for much help with editing the book.

PREFACE

The merger of Massey-Harris and Ferguson occurred in 1953 when I was nine years old. I was at an impressionable age as most youngsters would have been. But I was also a farmer's son and a part of a considerable farming family on my father's side. Both Massey-Harris and Ferguson were part of my every day language and experience. Next door at my grandfather's farm the yard was still full of by then mostly retired Massey-Harris tractors (the pre-war Wallis style U frame types) and implements. His farm was virtually adjacent to the Massey-Harris factory in Manchester and he had tested M-H equipment for the company since pre-war days. I can just recall the arrival of the first Ferguson tractor on the family farms – my father had bought one new in 1948 when I was a mere four years old. Later another second-hand one was to arrive on my grandfather's farm. Initially they worked alongside the old M-H tractors.

Famous names also visited my grandfather's house and frequently came up in conversation, though sadly I was just a bit too young to recall seeing any of them. They included James Duncan, President of Massey-Harris, Lionel Harper the Manager of Massey-Harris in the U.K. and Tom Carroll, Massey's world-famous

Tom Carroll, M-H's world-famous combine designer was a visitor to my grand father's farm. Here he is seen on an M-H 744D Tractor at the M-H Kilmarnock factory.

Above: One of the last of the famous Wallis design, M-H "U" frame tractors. An M-H styled 1938 Pacemaker Tractor at a ploughing demonstration in Scotland. Note the rare fitting of wheel weights.

Right: Tom Carroll, Massey's world-famous combine designer seen here in his "hands on" mode working on an M-H 21 Combine fitted with Rice Tracks.

combine designer. Also, my Dad's new Ferguson tractor was, after its first summer season, loaned to Massey-Harris for a full inspection to work out what the real opposition was. Apparently it spent six weeks in Massey's Barton Dock Road factory just a short way up the road from our farm.

To me these are wonderful childhood memories. The sight of them. The smell of them – all petrol/TVO (Kerosene) engines. The talk about them – endless debates about their respective merits. Watching them at work and driving them from a very early age – a pleasure now denied to my son's generation because of safety regulations. I recall that I learnt to drive sat on my father's knee on the Ferguson, then progressing to solo operation as soon as legs were long enough. The old Massey-Harris tractors were more favourable to small lads with their hand clutches – no need for long legs! Quite unwittingly I had experienced two totally different driving experiences. Firstly, the by now dinosaur Massey-Harris U frames, some of them on steel wheels, and secondly the sophisticated Ferguson which incorporated the most important advance in tractor design of the 20th century – the Ferguson System of linkage and weight transfer between implement and tractor. I had also experienced two different tractor and equipment cultures – the more "blacksmith" style of M-H equipment and the highly specified engineering of Ferguson equipment – factors which would be forever in the minds of the two company workforces as they merged.

By the time that I was nine, the family had also replaced the binder (M-H needless to say) with a combine harvester – again M-H – which was hired each year from a nearby farmer. I didn't at the time appreciate that this hired M-H 726 combine was a recent descendant of the now famous M-H No. 21 combine which had become the world's first truly successful mass produced self-propelled combine. As a child I had heard the post-war talk of the glory and fame it had achieved in the wartime Harvest Brigade activities in North America.

I was indeed fortunate in my childhood to have had the practical experience of the three essentials of what was to go into the Massey-Harris and Ferguson merger – the M-H combine, the Ferguson tractor and the out-dated* M-H tractor designs.

*In fact I missed out on the wartime and post-war M-H design tractors. The U frame tractors referred to were the pre-war tractors. However the post-war tractors were still grossly inferior in design terms to the revolutionary Ferguson tractor and integral Ferguson System.

At the merger I witnessed the Massey-Harris sign on the nearby factory change to Massey-Harris-Ferguson and I knew instinctively that something major had occurred. By the time I was 14 the name was to be abbreviated to Massey-Ferguson and the signs changed yet again! It was at about this time that the family bought their first combine harvester – a second-hand Massey-Harris 726 with Morris Commercial petrol/TVO engine. This subsequently gave me endless pleasure as I drove it extensively.

By the age of 14, I was aware that Massey-Ferguson was coming to be a major force in the world as I increasingly read the farming magazines each week. Since then there have been no further name changes

An M-H 744D Tractor stretched to full width in the Kilmarnock factory showroom.

The Ferguson Tractor could do anything!

Tom Caroll at the wheel of a German built M-H 630S which was similar in size to the UK built M-H 735.

despite many changes to the structure of the company – other than of course the subsequent dropping of the hyphen to become Massey Ferguson.

I never could get Massey-Harris and Ferguson out of my head. They became my hobby both mentally and practically, so much so that I have now written eight books on the history of Massey Ferguson, collected a shed full of tractors and, according to my wife, accumulated a house full of literature relating to them and their implements.

It occurred to me that MASSEY-HARRIS-FERGUSON is now an almost forgotten company name. It only lasted through six calendar years. But it was the formative period of Massey-Ferguson, an era which I believe deserves recording in its own right for the vintage agricultural machinery movement. It involved the coming together of two quite different workforces from the Massey-Harris and Ferguson companies. Massey-Harris, being a very old company with a traditional structure and management with a strength in harvesting equipment but a dated

tractor range and Ferguson, led by its founder Harry Ferguson, which had advanced engineering designs and a world-beating tractor. Both had achieved world-wide reputations and sales and it seemed an ideal marriage.

I have been very fortunate to come into contact with a lot of people who worked for Massey-Harris-Ferguson and/or the two individual companies before the merger. They gladly gave their time to recall their memories and they were so extensive that they became the basis of this book. As the memories accumulated with me I realised that there was no better way to recall the atmosphere and events of the merger period. Their memories have enabled me to compile what I believe is a very different type of book and I owe a deep debt of gratitude to them all.

The first M-F Tractor to roll off the Banner Lane factory line after M-F acquired the factory. August 31st 1959.

BACKGROUND

TO MASSEY-HARRIS AND FERGUSON

Two Companies

The merger of Massey-Harris and Ferguson in 1953 was by any standards a high profile event in the world of farm machinery. It involved the merger of two world renown companies whose personalities and products were, to say the least, dissimilar.

The two companies became Massey-Harris-Ferguson, rather a mouthful of a name, which was to be abandoned and become Massey-Ferguson after only four years in December 1957. These were to be four eventful years in which the two long-standing senior executives who merged the companies – Harry Ferguson and James Duncan for Massey-Harris - were to leave the scene in respectively only the first and third years after the merger. Overall control was then taken by Albert Thornbrough in 1956 following the resignation of James Duncan.

Not only did the M-H-F period see a near complete change of executives, but it witnessed a difficult financial period, the adoption of a two line policy in which the Massey-Harris and Ferguson product lines were maintained as separate identities, the inevitable difficulties of merging two company administrations and workforces, and the necessary evolution of new company policies, products and identity.

Whilst the courtship was smooth, as in any marriage partners have to get to know each other and merge their identities. The two line policy was finally abandoned in 1957 but it was not until 1964 that new composite world-wide MF tractor lines were released on the market in the form of the MF 100 and 1000 series tractors. In the meantime a series of models were marketed including larger tractors from Oliver and Minneapolis Moline which were re-badged and

Daniel Massey founded the Massey company in 1847, later taking over Alanson Harris and then called the company Massey-Harris.

Harry Ferguson founded the Ferguson group of companies. Here he is seen demonstrating the safety features of his tractors using one of his models – now highly sought-after as collectors' items

liveried to MF specifications. However, two tractors, the Ferguson TO 35 (later MF 35) and MF 65 which were introduced in 1954 and 1957 respectively, were to be the design foundations for the MF 100 and 1000 series 1964 tractors.

The accepted theory at the time of the merger was that it was an ideal marriage. Massey-Harris had a global reputation for its harvesting equipment, particularly its combine harvesters, as well as being a supplier of a very wide range of reputable, albeit outdated agricultural tractors, and implements generally. Ferguson on the other hand had the premier agricultural engineering invention of the 20th century in the form of his integrated tractor and implement automatic weight transfer "Ferguson System" with all the advantages of design and

operational economies that came with it.

The M-H-F years did however start the laying of solid foundations for the new company. Major acquisitions were to be H.V. McKay Massey-Harris (Pty) Ltd. of Australia in 1955, makers of the Sunshine brand line of farm equipment; and Mid-Western Industries Inc. of Kansas in 1957 which took them into the industrial equipment business. These plus the merger with Ferguson gave the company great increase in manufacturing capacity around the world in addition to modernisation and expansion of M-H facilities which had existed at the time of the merger

Following the dropping of the two line policy in 1957 very significant company acquisitions followed very soon with Perkins in 1959 and Landini in 1960. The M-H-F years also saw conceptual seeds being

Massey-Harris was a very big company – even in early days as evidenced from this 1913 logo which was used on both catalogues and implements of the day.

Perhaps one of the greatest tractor salesmen of all time? Harry Ferguson addresses the audience gathered for Ferguson Tractor and Implement demonstration in the USA.

Harry Ferguson was dedicated to easing the toil of small farmers and nowhere more so than in his own native Northern Ireland. The McCurdy family of Whitepark Bay, still potato farming today, were early enthusiasts for Ferguson tractors. Here they are mowing their corn with a Ferguson Tractor and Mower, gathering it by hand, tying it in sheaves and then placing the sheaves in stooks. ©Brian Sinclair Photography, N. Ireland.

sown for the creation of an MF Special Operations Division which could handle the establishment of overseas manufacturing operations either directly or under licence. This division was established in 1959.

At the time of the merger Massey-Harris was still very much in a post-war reconstruction and expansion mood. James Duncan had fought for the renewal and expansion of facilities in Europe and these had started to reward the company well.

In 1946 Ferguson had suffered the collapse of his tractor manufacturing agreement with Ford in America and had to rapidly re-start production from scratch in two plants in the immediate post-war period - not an inconsiderable feat given post-war materials shortages and other regulatory constraints of the period. The first factory was in Coventry, UK and owned by the Standard Motor Co., which started producing in 1946, and the second built by Ferguson was in Detroit, USA which started producing in 1948.

Thus we see M-H as a long established company in a phase of global expansion, whereas Ferguson had only re-consolidated his tractor manufacturing operation a mere 6-7 years before the merger with Massey-Harris.

It was perhaps a sadness that Ferguson and Duncan were not younger men at the time of the merger. During their careers both had pushed through significant technical innovations in farm machinery. James Duncan had nurtured the development of Massey-Harris combine harvesters and post-war expansion of Massey-Harris's European facilities, whilst Harry Ferguson had invented his now world-famous "Ferguson System". Both had shown global vision for their products and astonishing perseverance in the war and post-war period. Both had fought numerous battles for the place of their products in the world market place. Both had astonishing reserves of energy which they appear to have given unselfishly to their respective organisations. Both were exceptionally skilled at personal hands on marketing of their products.

Neither man was in the prime of life or health at the merger and eventually Duncan had to resign on health grounds. Ferguson's age and declining health may have contributed to his lack of will to keep battling on for what he believed in for the new M-H-F organisation. Instead he seems to have departed the agricultural scene, possibly tired of it, in an endeavour to make his mark on the automobile scene with his

highly successful four-wheel drive innovations. But this post M-H-F fame was to be short-lived because he died in 1960.

The Philosophy of Harry Ferguson's Operations

The 1948 Harry Ferguson Inc. Annual Report for his American Operations contains a page devoted to his philosophy for minimal involvement in, and ownership of, manufacturing and marketing operations. They highlight his long-standing strategy of minimal involvement in manufacturing and marketing – something which he was only dragged into when desperate occasions arose as in the break with Ford for manufacturing his Ferguson System tractors in America. The two succinct paragraphs which made the point are titled:

The Nature of the Massey-Harris and Ferguson

A Policy of DECENTRALIZATION

IN PRODUCTION

With decentralized production, Ferguson can employ the best manufacturing facilities for each implement or component, while concentrating on quality and product improvement through engineering and research. Also, through decentralized manufacture, implements are produced in the area of greatest use, thus effecting substantial freight savings to the farmer. By purchasing its tractor components and implements from manufacturing specialists, Ferguson gains full advantage of decentralized manufacture and the "know-how" of such specialists – with the same "sub-contracting" formula which won the battle of production in World War II.

IN DISTRIBUTION

Ferguson Tractors and Ferguson System Implements are distributed through independent distributors and dealers. In distribution, as in production, this decentralization results in a spreading of opportunity and responsibility, a proper delegating of functions and obligations in respective spheres of operation, sharing, protecting and assuring profits in each local situation. This policy nourishes and develops the economic life of local communities, and furthers healthy, competitive, free enterprise.

Organisations at the Merger in 1953

The following table is an endeavour to present a concise summary of the nature of the two companies as they entered the merger. The long established nature of Massey-Harris and its vast manufacturing capacity are in stark contrast to Ferguson's one factory and relatively short history

A postcard showing the Harry Ferguson. Inc. Tractor factory at Detroit.

	Massey-Harris	Ferguson
Management style	Mature company style operation with significant delegation of authority	Young company still dominated by founder who exerted considerable detail control over senior staff
Age of company/length of involvement with agricultural machinery	Started by Daniel Massey in 1847	First Ferguson implement (plough) demonstrated 1917. Sold Overtime tractors in 1st world war.
Mergers and acquisitions of other machinery manufactures	Numerous, starting in 1848	Essentially none other than of minor nature
Age of senior executive	James Duncan, 63	Harry Ferguson, 68
Key ambitions of senior executive	Continued global company expansion in manufacturing and marketing. In particular post war strengthening of production in Europe.	Developing four-wheel drive systems for cars may have come to fascinate Ferguson more than tractors
Global visions of senior executives	Very anti-communist but recognised need to develop a dialogue with the USSR	Believed in a global price reducing scheme to better the world economy through the agricultural sector
Major equipment strength	Combine harvesters and harvesting generally. But also a very wide range of tractors and implements and other supporting equipment for rural economies	Ferguson system tractors and integrated implements
No. of tractors produced in year before merger	TOTAL 28,912 of which: 17,083 at Racine, USA 1,150 at Woodstock, Canada 2,546 at Kilmarnock, UK 8,133 at Marquette, France	TOTAL 67,381 of which: 48,060 at Coventry, UK(2) 17,314 at Detroit, USA (2) 2,007 at St. Denis, France
No. of tractors produced to time of merger	approx. 282,988 (1929-1952 incl)	approx. 735,997 (excl. those produced by Ford which infringed Ferguson patents)
No. of combine harvesters sold in year before	23,096(1)	0
No. of combine harvesters made	139,766 (1946-1952 incl)	0
Implement source	Mainly in house	Mainly from outside suppliers
No. of owned factories	Toronto works 1,.904,028 sq ft Elector-Forge Division, Toronto, 21,554 sq ft Market St works, Brantford , 554,257 sq ft "M" Foundry, Brantford, 15,866 sq ft Verity Works, Brantford, 511,754 sq ft Woodstock Works, Woodstock 304,800 sq ft Manchester, England 337,034 sq ft Kilmarnock, Scotland 461,950 sq ft Marquette, France 602,881 sq ft Westhoven, Germany 85,319 sq ft Eschwege, Germany 75,518 sq ft Racine, Wisconsin 1,258,886 sq ft Batavia, New York 918,962 sq ft Fowler, California 67,007 sq ft	Detroit 215,520 sq ft

Value of company at merger	Approx. 150,000,000 dollars (assets + land + buildings + equipment. 1952 M-H annual report)	$ 16,385,000 paid by M-H (3)
Turnover in last financial year	Total sales 224,806,540 dollars	£ 20,900,000 at Coventry (2) $ 35,700,000 at Detroit (2) ($70,967,337 net sales at Detroit in fiscal 1952) (4)
Net profit last year before merger	9 million USD	£ 221,385 at Coventry (2) - $ 104,331 at Detroit (2)
No. of staff	18,930 world-wide (1952 M-H annual report)	2,200 employed in the two factories
Sales branches	Yes, world-wide. 15 branches in U.S.A.	None owned, but Ferguson holdings in many countries. No branches in U.K – distribution from factories. Export territories of Europe, S. Africa, Australia, N. Zealand operated from Coventry
Distributors and dealers	2400 dealers in N America alone	Independent distributors and dealers. 66 distributors in 78 countries. 28 in U.S.A. and 6 in Canada. About 200 sales outlets in U.K – dealers and sub dealers. 100 small dealers in Ireland.
No. of countries represented in	106	Numerous: see table below.....
No. of countries manufacturing in	USA, Canada, UK, France, Germany, Australia, S. Africa	UK, USA
Use of Perkins diesel engines in tractors	Started – 744D tractor in 1948 in U.K.	No
Use of other diesel engines	Yes, Continental Motor Company	Yes, Standard Motor Company
Offering lamp oil tractors	No	Yes
Current defence equipment production	Yes, Tanks and mortar bomb contracts	None
Offering household equipment	Yes, mainly Canada e.g. freezers, washing machines	Never
Offering small farm equipment	Yes, mainly Canada e.g. Milking machines, cream separators	Never
Offering LPG tractors	Yes	No
Still making horse drawn equipment	Yes	No, never did
Offering industrial tractors	Revived 1953 after lapse since early 1930's	Yes, since Ferguson Brown era

1. In fiscal year ending Oct. 31st 1953
2. In 10 months
3. Note that this did not include production facilities in UK as these were owned by the Standard Motor Co. MF were to buy these later which really added to the "overall" price of buying the whole scope of Ferguson operations
4. This includes some of settlement from Ford law suit

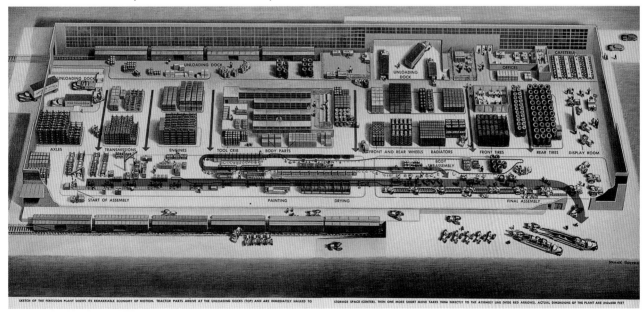

Plan of the only factory which Harry Ferguson owned – the Detroit tractor plant.

M-H had a 640 acres Testing Farm outside Toronto, Canada where their Tractor and Equipment range was tested both on special test tracks and in general farm work.

A Obstacle Course No. 1
B Angled Paving Blocks.
C Hurricane Dust Tunnel.
D 3-Foot Deep Water Bath.
E Heavy Gumbo Mud Bog.
F Levee Obstacle Course No. 2
G Ramp and Gradient Pad.

at *Massey-Harris*
testing really gets down to earth

An historic moment for Harry Ferguson. The first TO 20 Tractor of the line at his newly built Detroit factory on Nov.11th, 1948. His break with the Ford Motor Co. because of their infringement of his patents caused him to have to build his own factory which was done in short time. The driver is Mr Nils Lou, the Ferguson Plant Manager, surrounded by his staff.

Massey-Harris's main tractor plant was at Racine, Wisconsin. This is a 1957 shot showing on-going tractor manufacture. Within a very few years the plant was closed and tractor production for Massey-Ferguson concentrated on what was formerly Harry Ferguson's Detroit plant.

The Financial and Market Nature of Harry Ferguson's U.K. Products

From archive material, the following three tables have been assembled. The actual figures were used by Massey-Harris in their deliberations about buying Ferguson. They give some idea of the profitability levels that he was working at, and the extent of the overseas markets which he had so successfully penetrated.

Unit profits 1953

Item	Profit/unit	Gross profit at June 30th 1953 as per trading accounts
Petrol tractor	£10.10.0d	3.55%
V.O. Tractor	£14.5.0d	4.57%
Lamp oil tractor	£18.0.0d	7.08%
Diesel tractor	£19.15.0d	4.82%
Implements		17.06%
Spares		15.9%
Accessories		18.23%

Contribution to sales

Item	Sales	Gross margin
Tractors	£23,027,000	£1,017,000
Implements	£4,635,000	£781,000
Spares	£1,505,000	£230,000
Accessories	£31,000	£6,000
Note: Tractors are 74% of sales value but only 47% of the gross margin		

Principal Tractor Exports from the U.K.

Market	1952	1953 (6 months)
Canada	4952	1150
Argentina	1	0
Brazil	382	0
Cuba	252	175
Peru	120	51
Uraguay	180	0
Chile	0	171
Rest of Latin America	296	76
Australia	5686	3540
New Zealand	2389	1263
South Sea Islands	139	64
South Africa	1332	1118
East Africa	352	85
West Africa	130	238
Rest of Africa (except French Africa)	312	173
France (Hotchkiss)	0	1098
France (other)	3038	822
Algeria	623	181
Morocco	272	50
Tunisia	187	117
Rest of French Africa	18	39
Middle East	332	209
Turkey	2904	0
Greece	103	32
Austria	114	57
Belgium	1074	548
Denmark	6377	2605
Finland	2615	13
Germany	642	312
Holland	1005	316
Iceland	260	88
Italy	2233	841
Norway	2782	1097
Portugal	203	76
Spain	314	94
Sweden	4546	2680
Rest of Europe	111	0

Ferguson's Trading Outlook for the Merger Year

The immediate outlook for the Ferguson companies in the merger year was poor as were analyses for the Massey-Harris company in their deliberations about a merger. This data is from archive material:

Estimated Profits for 12 months to December 31st 1953

Harry Ferguson Ltd. England	Harry Ferguson Inc. Detroit
£225,000 (630,000 dollars)	133,000 dollars

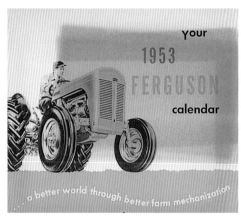

Ferguson's last calendar in the USA was in 1953. Today these are highly collectable and often contain good photos of Ferguson equipment.

The Harry Ferguson Companies at the Time of the Merger

One of the exhibits pertaining to the final merger agreement was a listing of the various Ferguson companies around the world which were to be included in the agreement. These were:

Harry Ferguson Ltd* (UK)
Harry Ferguson Incorporated** (USA)
Harry Ferguson of Australia Ltd
Harry Ferguson of New Zealand Ltd
Harry Ferguson of India Ltd
Harry Ferguson of Pakistan Ltd
Harry Ferguson of Japan Ltd
Harry Ferguson of South Africa Ltd
Harry Ferguson S.A. (Pty.) Ltd
Harry Ferguson of Sweden Ltd
Harry Ferguson de France S.A.
Harry Ferguson of Belgium Ltd
Harry Ferguson of Italy Ltd
Harry Ferguson of Germany Ltd
Shorrock Superchargers Ltd
Hodgkiss Oilburners Ltd

* This included Harry Ferguson's specialised machinery development facility on Fletchamstead Highway in Coventry.

** This included a development facility in Ferguson Park at the Detroit tractor assembly plant.

Note: Harry Ferguson Research Ltd. was not included in the merger deal. This organisation in Coventry was retained and was at the time actively incubating new Ferguson tractor and car designs.

It is also noted that Ferguson had pioneered the start of licensed production of his tractors overseas in the form of tractor assembly in India. This operation ultimately became TAFE – Tractors and Farm Equipment. Licensed production was later taken up by Massey Ferguson in several countries.

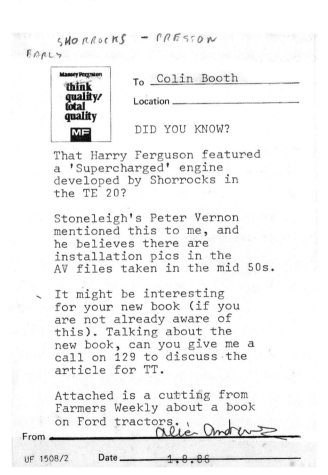

SHORROCKS – PRESTON
REPLY

To Colin Booth

Location

DID YOU KNOW?

That Harry Ferguson featured a 'Supercharged' engine developed by Shorrocks in the TE 20?

Stoneleigh's Peter Vernon mentioned this to me, and he believes there are installation pics in the AV files taken in the mid 50s.

It might be interesting for your new book (if you are not already aware of this). Talking about the new book, can you give me a call on 129 to discuss the article for TT.

Attached is a cutting from Farmers Weekly about a book on Ford tractors.

From

UF 1508/2   Date   1.8.86

Shorrock Superchargers Ltd. is one of the less well-known of the companies owned by Harry Ferguson. This 1986 M-F memo makes reference to the company. It is addressed to Colin Booth who wrote one of the first ever books on Ferguson tractors.

Signing the contract for Harry Ferguson's Detroit Tractor factory. L. R. Herman Klemm, Charles Herrmeyer, Phil Page, Bob Surridge, contractor seated, HoraceD'Angelo and contractor.

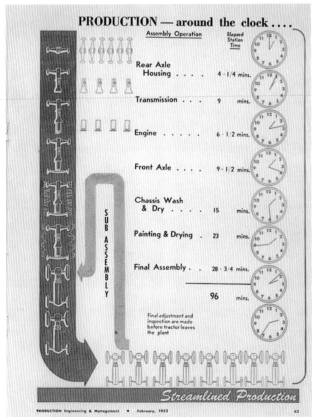

A bird's-eye view of the assembly line where tractors are nearing completion.

This page and next: Ferguson TO 20 Tractor production at the Ferguson Detroit, USA factory – the only factory owned by Harry Ferguson.

Horace D'Angelo, General Manager and Executive Vice President of Harry Ferguson, Inc., drives the first of the new Ferguson "30" tractors off the assembly line. The tractor plant produces 250 tractors during an 8-hour shift.

> Materials handling in the Ferguson tractor plant is regulated efficiently. Here a lift truck picks up a specially designed metal rack, which holds a unit of four engines. The cost and time required in the handling of materials is considerably reduced by methods like this.

< At the first station on the main assembly line, the axle housing is lowered into place. Specifications from sub-contractors are rigidly followed.

> Materials handling in the Ferguson tractor plant is regulated efficiently. Here a lift truck picks up a specially designed metal rack, which holds a unit of four engines. The cost and time required in the handling of materials is considerably reduced by methods like this.

< At the first station on the main assembly line, the axle housing is lowered into place. Specifications from sub-contractors are rigidly followed.

> Everything is done automatically. The painted chassis is carried by an overhead conveyor to the dryer.

Albert A. Thornbrough, vice-president and director of procurement, (center) and his department heads go over plans for sub-contracting parts.

Lift trucks deposit the component parts of the axle housing assembly, still in their metal pallets, on the sub-assembly line. The parts have been manufactured and pre-assembled by sub-contractors who are chosen largely on the basis of the cost and quality of their work.

Here the engine becomes an integral part of the tractor. Every operation all along the assembly line has been timed, and management knows just exactly how many men and how many motions are required to perform each operation.

< The chassis is sent through a unit which washes and drys it automatically after it has been assembled.

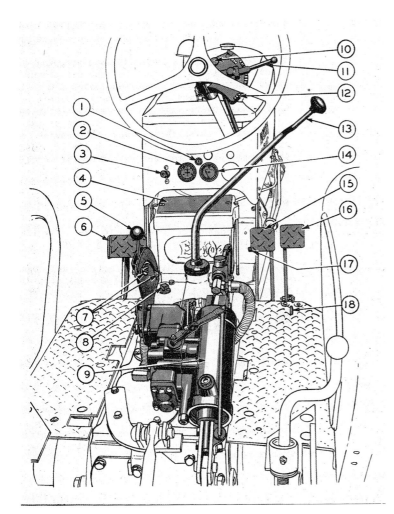

The hydraulic systems offered by M-H were no match for that of the "Ferguson System" where the hydraulic system fully integrated the combined performance and behaviour of both tractor and implement. M-H Hydraulics were just an "add on" for lifting and lowering implements as shown by these two diagrams of the hydraulics of a UK built M-H 744 tractor (bottom) and USA built M-H Colt tractor (top).

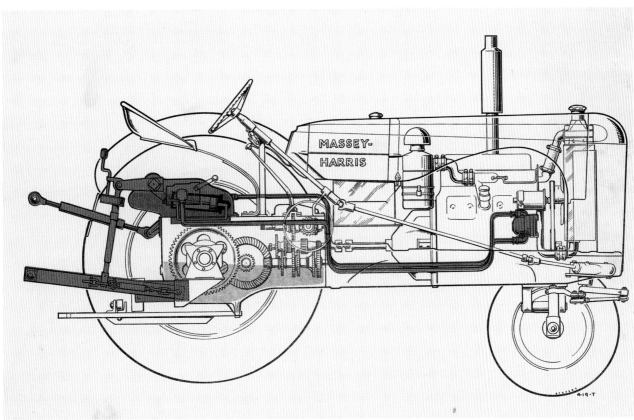

THE MERGER

In essence the merger was a product of negotiations between Harry Ferguson and James Duncan, the head of Massey-Harris in 1953. Serious negotiations appear to have started in April and the deal was struck on the twelfth of August.

Setting the Scene

The possibility of a relationship between Massey-Harris and Ferguson dated back to 1947. This had been precipitated by Ferguson's break with Ford in November 1946, and Ford's subsequent production of a tractor (the Ford 8N) similar to the one which was originally designed by Ferguson. It is recalled that Ford had produced Ferguson's tractor for him since 1939 in the form of the "Ford Ferguson". Ferguson desperately needed to re-establish production and marketing of a Ferguson tractor in North America, convinced that he could win back customers from Ford. In 1946 he had successfully established the production of the British Ferguson TE tractor which was providing much for the home and export markets, but he needed production within North America. He had also successfully sub-contracted implement manufacture in the U.K.

And so it was that in 1947 Ferguson first met with a Vice-President of Massey-Harris, J.M. Tucker, and subsequently, for the first time, the Massey-Harris President James Duncan. Ferguson basically wanted Massey-Harris to build tractors for him. They met in Detroit where Duncan was given a demonstration of the tractor by Ferguson. It is reported that the two got along well, but in the final analysis the Massey-Harris board agreed that it was not in their interests to accept Ferguson's proposals. Duncan records that they never had any regrets and that he and Ferguson had formed a very amicable relationship with Ferguson having a high opinion of the Massey-Harris staff. It is also reported that Duncan again met Ferguson in 1949 in connection with manufacturing certain machines for him, but again nothing became of the meeting.

In 1952 there was a need for Massey-Harris to increase production at their Scottish plant in Kilmarnock which manufactured combines and balers. In 1953 events conspired. An approach was made to Ferguson's General Manager Alan Botwood to see if they were still interested in Massey-Harris building Ferguson's proposed side-mounted combine. Although Botwood and Duncan were able to agree manufacture by Massey-Harris and marketing through Ferguson's organization, a week later Ferguson vetoed the idea.

However Ferguson, who had been ill in Ireland and was recently returned to the U.K. expressed his wish to meet Duncan and invited him to his home where he was convalescing. At his home, Abbotswood at Stow-in-the-Wold, they duly met and had what was probably only their third meeting ever. Ferguson had a deep conviction to associate with Duncan because of his business success. Ferguson was concerned about how he himself was ageing. Duncan was asked to give up his Presidency and Chairmanship of Massey-Harris and become an equal partner with Ferguson, and to take over full management. Duncan declined the offer, Ferguson suggested he was making a big mistake and they went for a polite walk round the garden then to eventually take tea.

Then Ferguson suggested that in order to retain Duncan's services he would sell him the company progressively starting with the Detroit Ferguson operation. Duncan was aware of the marginal financial state of both the American and British Ferguson operations and declared that he doubted whether he could recommend it to the Massey-Harris Board.

However subsequently Duncan and some of his men met Ferguson at the Detroit Plant where opinions were formed on the strengths and weaknesses of the operation. The Massey-Harris Board still thought it an undesirable venture and Ferguson was advised accordingly.

Following this Ferguson again invited Duncan to England to discuss a broader "proposition". The Massey-Harris Board then authorised Duncan to fully evaluate both the U.K. and American Ferguson companies and negotiate a deal with Ferguson.

Ferguson wanted Duncan badly as his second business partner in life, the first having been Henry Ford.

It is important to remember that both Ferguson and Massey-Harris did not just have a merger on their minds. They had to carry on the normal everyday affairs of their two businesses, continue with on-going developments (Ferguson had a separate new tractor design on each side of the Atlantic, new implement designs for his new larger tractor, and three completely new side-mounted implements evolving. Meanwhile Massey-Harris was evolving its new combines).

The Involvement of the Standard Motor Company, Manufacturers of the Ferguson Tractor in the UK

Sir John Black, the owner of the Standard Motor Co. that produced the Ferguson tractor in UK, said that the introduction of diesel engine into Ferguson tractor range had proved an outstanding success. Nearly 50% of their tractors were now fitted with diesel engines. At the existing time they were producing over 1000 tractors a week, and they were going up to 1250 or more in New Year. Plant and equipment had been ordered for manufacture of a new and larger Ferguson tractor (known as the LTX when it was under development and to be designated the Ferguson TE 60 when produced). This was an additional model to present types manufactured by the company and designed to operate a four furrow plough. They and the Ferguson company believed that it would prove to be another outstanding success, particularly in the dollar area. Since the company had undertaken manufacture of Ferguson tractors for Harry Ferguson Ltd., 309,244 had been delivered.

It had become apparent over the previous 18 months that it was necessary to either establish manufacturing facilities in France for Ferguson tractors or to lose the large business that Harry Ferguson had built up there. Subject to the approval of the French government, Standard Motor Co was about

The site of all Ferguson Tractor manufacture in the U.K was the Standard Motor Co. Works in Banner Lane, Coventry. It was owned by Sir John Black who made the tractors for Harry Ferguson. This factory was not included in the merger deal but M-F went on to acquire it in 1959.

to conclude an arrangement on a partnership basis with Messrs. Hotchkiss, the French motor car and armaments firm, to form a new company to be known as Société Standard-Hotchkiss.

Standard had amalgamated the interests of their Australian Associated Company and Standard Cars Ltd. The latter company had been their distributor for more than 20 years and they formed a new company "Standard Motor Products Ltd." with a nominal capital of £(Australian) 5 million. The new company had been formed with the aim of undertaking assembly and progressive manufacture of Standard and Triumph cars and commercial vehicles under a 25 year agreement. It was further proposed that the new company should include plans for producing Ferguson tractors as and when the need arose. Australia remained the largest potential export market for tractors.

Notes by J. S. Duncan to the M-H Board on the Benefits of an Association with Ferguson

The main points of advantage and concerns of an association with Ferguson were identified by James Duncan to his company board to be as follows:
- Adding the Ferguson line would bring great prestige
- It would bring the most advanced engineering practices known to the industry
- M-H would inherit at low cost a backlog of 200,000 tractor and implement sales in the U.S.A
- Could increase dealer network to 4000 or more
- Would be marketing the original Ferguson products, which in some form or other have been copied by all manufacturers
- Have the advantage of the inventiveness of Harry Ferguson and presumably the services of Herman Klemm (Ferguson's head of engineering in his Detroit operation)
- Strengthen position in export field
- Fair assumption that Ferguson and Klemm know more about the application of the Ferguson System than any other manufacturer
- Ford has the dominant sales position over Ferguson at present in the ratio of 6:1 (this was due to Ford infringing Ferguson patents and producing the Ford 8N tractor which Ferguson had successfully challenged in court and received compensation). Were it not for this a merger would be of unquestionable advantage. However we must recognise

that if we cannot compete against Ford with Ferguson 2-plow tractor we cannot either with our M-H 22 or Mustang. Our own Pitt tractor (under design and development) would not fare any better even though the Pitt tractor shows certain advantages but which have yet to be proven
- Should not look on Ford as the sole competition, but also compete with International Harvester, John Deere, Oliver etc.
- Our investigations show beyond doubt that large sales of Ferguson-Ford type tractor are due much to their concentrated sales organisation and line of well designed equipment as to the tractor itself
- If we turn down this proposal because we believe Ferguson cannot compete with Ford, then we must admit that our present line, or with the Pitt tractor, we could not compete either and therefore would be tantamount to abandoning the 2-plow tractor field.
- By buying Ferguson we are presumably putting ourselves in the lead as regards the 3-4-plow tractor. If it is an outstanding success then it will cut sales of our M-H 33 and M-H 44 tractors
- Ford with his new tractor has undoubted advantages over Ferguson this year and will hold to next year which the Ferguson 3-4 plough tractor would then seize. But Ford might introduce Fordson-Major in the U.K.
- A Massey-Harris-Ferguson dealership with 2-plow and 3-4 plough tractor range and more up to date engineering of implements would be more desirable one than Ford's, especially as it would carry with it M-H combines, lugging tractors and pull-behind implements.
- Great stress placed on the engineering quality of the Ferguson designed implements stemming from Harry Ferguson's genius and may never be duplicated by Ford just as it has not yet been duplicated by anyone in the orthodox implement industry.
- Advantage of immediate increased production in existing M-H works in U.S.A., U.K. and perhaps France
- ..... Basically, we must ask ourselves if the trend is towards the Ferguson concept or the old line implement company concept of engineering.

James Duncan also noted the following salient sales points to his board:

- 1,255,000 Ferguson type tractors sold to date including Ford 8N tractors which infringed Ferguson patents
- In 1952 Ford and Ferguson sold 24% of all tractors sold in U.S.A. and 50% of all tractors in two plough class
- In U.K. where Ford once dominated market with 80-90% Fordson Majors, Ferguson now sells about 61% of all tractors
- All manufacturers have now followed Ferguson's

Three photos of what are believed to be the prototype M-H Pitt Tractor designed for M-H by Professor Arnold Pitt. It was hoped that it might compete with the Ferguson tractor. Len Boon (see acknowledgements) recalled seeing the Pitt Tractor on show at M-H's showrooms in Toronto.

Ferguson – a winner every time. Winning times for an American farmer with a TO 25 Tractor.

James Duncan's views on how a merger might proceed were expressed to his Board as follows:

- M-H purchase full control of U.S.A. Corporation calling new company Massey-Harris-Ferguson.
- Sort out M-H and Ferguson dealers in the USA to arrive at total of 3000-3500 down from M-H's 2,400 plus Ferguson's 2000
- In amalgamating the two organisations, retain specialised forces of tractor salesmen, new dealers to have access to full line.
- No immediate radical changes to lines
- But, cut the M-H No 22, Mustang and Colt tractors and replace with the Ferguson tractor
- Manufacture in M-H plants many of implements made outside and possibly take over some Ferguson tractor jobs. Ferguson tractor to continue to be made at Detroit
- As Ferguson's new tractor came into production

it would be made at Racine. At first it would be an addition to the line, but if Ferguson was right about its quality it would eventually replace the M-H 33 and 44 and perhaps the M-H 55.

Ferguson Plans

Ferguson plans at the time were to increase their line by the addition of the following important tractor and implements:

- a new large tractor
- two new models of the present small tractor
- non-reversible disc harrow
- side-mounted mower
- one-way disc
- two row middle buster
- forage harvester
- four row corn planter
- four row cultivator

Harry Ferguson Ltd.

Coventry

Telegrams "Farming"
Telephone Coventry 5533

London Office:
37, Davies Street, W.1.

Gentlemen,

May 13th, 1953.

OUR NEW BIG TRACTOR.

Deliveries of this should start in the Spring of next year. Samples have been on continuous secret testing over the country during the past twelve months. The performance is really superlative and this machine will make more history for us in the tractor world.

You may well ask why we did not market a big tractor many years ago. The answer is that the Ferguson System, as embodied in the small tractor, was quite unsuitable for the big tractor. It would not control the bigger implements successfully. We came to this conclusion ten years ago and, since then, have been working continuously on an entirely new system which, with many other new inventions, is embodied in this new machine.

At this time, in view of the patent situation throughout the world, it would not be wise to demonstrate the new tractor nor to publish anything about our new inventions. We do not propose to demonstrate and publish details until early next year. In the meantime we will give you just a few facts so that you can start making your plans for a rapid and prosperous development of sales:-

1. The new tractor will have a smooth, very economical Diesel engine of about 48 h.p.

2. We have put long years into the problem of packing the soil and are glad to tell you that the weight per square inch on the land is little more than the present tractor.

3. The machine will pull a 4-furrow plough in all general conditions and on hilly land almost as easily, for example, as the small tractor will pull a 2-furrow.

4. Our new tractor will mark a new era in farming machinery. The farmers of the world urgently need standardisation in tractors and the equipment for them. That we have provided in full measure. Generally speaking, the implements and equipment

Directors: Harry G. Ferguson (Chairman) A. Botwood (Managing) Maureen A. Ferguson Elizabeth M. Sheldon L.G. Reid E.W. Young J.J. Wallace

Ferguson Ltd.
Coventry

-2-

Continuation Sheet

will be interchangeable.   A farmer who has a 3-ton
trailer for the present tractor will, for example,
be able to use it on the large tractor. He will
also be able to use, with reservations, the tillage
and row-crop equipment for the small tractor.
One wrench will suffice for all adjustments of all
the machinery. No longer will the farmer need to
have two or more sets of equipment working on
different principles as is now the case. Just
think how this will simplify the problem of
education on farms where both sizes of tractor will
be needed. We consider that this achievement of
standardising farm machinery for the first time in
history will have far-reaching consequences
throughout the world.

5.   The price has not yet been fixed but it will be
moderate. The Standard Motor Company, with its
usual energy and efficiency, is equipping a plant
with the most modern production machinery that can
be bought. We will, therefore, have a high-class
product at the lowest possible price.

6.   The following new implements will be available:-

4-furrow 8", 10", 12" and 14" Ploughs

A 3-furrow 16" Plough

A 13-tine Tiller

A 5-ton Trailer

THE CHALLENGE CAMPAIGN.

So extraordinary is the performance of the new tractor
that we intend to challenge not merely the largest wheeled
tractors but also the crawler-type, for every job on the farm.

A new Challenge Campaign will be organised for this
work. This is one reason why we urge upon all our Dealers to
develop the present Challenge Campaign for the small tractor
with the utmost energy. The more experience they gain in this
campaign with the small tractor, the more successful will be
their campaign with the big tractor.

The standardisation of farm machinery will make a big
appeal to farmers and this, in turn, should considerably
increase the sale of the small tractor.

YOUR RESOURCES.

We anticipate so much success for the new machine and

ᵍuson Ltd.
Coventry
                 -3-
Continuation Sheet

its range of implements that it will be necessary for you to make provision for more capital resources and more space for the efficient development of sales.

<u>ORDERS.</u>

We have been planning so that you could begin to book orders immediately. Naturally, any farmer will hesitate to order a new machine without full details of its design and performance. As we have said, it would not be advisable in all our interests to give these details at this time.

We have, therefore, planned that any farmer or industrialist can place an order for this machine and new implements without committing himself financially until the machine is demonstrated under his own conditions.

We attach sample of an Order Form we wish you to have printed locally. No details should be altered. This will enable you to begin booking orders immediately from your most progressive farmers who will thus secure the advantage of early delivery without any financial commitment.

The advantages of holding a large Order Book for this wonderful new tractor will be obvious to all. Quantity production means low price and quicker delivery to you. Will you, therefore, go forward with the <u>utmost vigour</u> in this great opportunity of helping your country's home and export trade through the establishment of another big new industry.

<u>YOUR REPLY TO THIS LETTER.</u>

Please:

1. Head your letter 'Attention Mr. Trevor Knox'.

2. Say what provision in capital and space you propose to make for the handling of the new machine.

3. As orders are received a copy of the Order Form should be forwarded to us immediately.

           Yours faithfully,
           for HARRY FERGUSON LTD.,

Harry Ferguson

HF/TG.

- single row corn picker and two row mounted corn picker
- 6 ft. side-mounted combine
- 9ft 6 in. side-mounted combine
- hay baler
- 3 ton trailer
- 3-4 mounted disc plow

These machines were planned for introduction commencing in 1954 and likely major production in 1955. M-H considered that their prestige would be increased by the addition of the Ferguson tractors and implements in the present line.

The Ferguson situation in the USA

Above: Fords had also made prototypes of a large tractor when they were producing the "Ford Tractor. Ferguson System" in conjunction with Harry Ferguson. The prototype never came to commercial production.

Right: A Ferguson Side Mounted Mower on a Ferguson TO-35 industrial style M-H-F Work Bull Tractor. The Mower had a counterbalanced drive for vibration-free operation.

Below: Cross-section detail of the British designed Ferguson Side-mounted Combine. 1956.

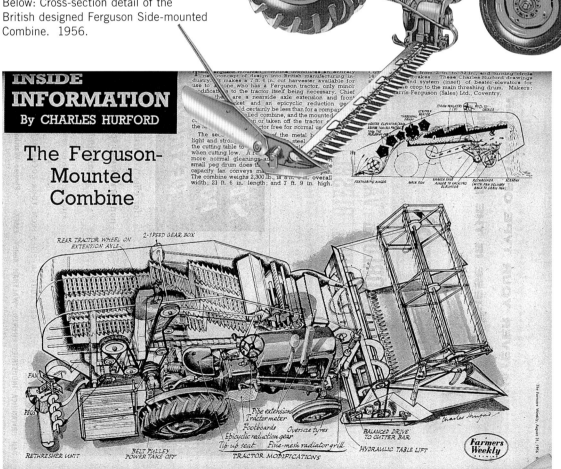

INSIDE INFORMATION
By CHARLES HURFORD

The Ferguson-Mounted Combine

Herman Klemm, head of Ferguson engineering in Detroit reported to Harry Ferguson in July a deteriorating sales situation. Ferguson replied with the following key points:

- I have never received a worse shock than the state of affairs which the letter disclosed
- The first and most vital thing to do is to put our present tractor (TO 30) right if all the troubles mentioned have not yet been put right
- Harry Ferguson Inc. (the USA company) is going to pieces before our eyes

Klemm in his reply to Harry Ferguson noted:

- Our plant has been closed from July 1st and won't re-open until August 10th
- Our Sales Division has been unable to ship more tractors....it was best to close the plant

The factory had also been affected by strikes at component suppliers, and there was a considerable inventory of unsold tractors at Detroit and elsewhere.

On the Toss of a Coin – August 12th 1953

One of the more enduring incidents of the final negotiations which has been widely reported is the tossing of a coin to settle the final price. As the negotiations were reaching their climax a million dollars separated the two sides. Harry Ferguson suggested that they toss a coin to settle the difference. The Massey-Harris team agreed. A half-crown coin was used, the UK's largest coin at that time and equal to $1/8$th of £1. Ferguson lost. Massey-Harris had the coin mounted for him on a silver humidor and suitably engraved with kind words. Len Boon was despatched to arrange the mounting.

It is the more amazing that this all happened in a car taking them to a demonstration. In the car were Ferguson, Duncan, Phillips and McDougland (the latter two both M-H directors). The car was stopped in front of the Lincoln Arms in Broadway in the Cotswolds.

When Ferguson later sold out his shares and resigned over differences of opinion concerning engineering and pricing in 1954, the same cigar humidor was passed around the M-H-F negotiators despite their frequent acrimonious and drawn out nature.

But the agreement made between Harry Ferguson and James Duncan of Massey-Harris still had to be ratified by the M-H board and the UK Board of Trade and the UK Treasury

A report of the tossing of the coin (source unknown).

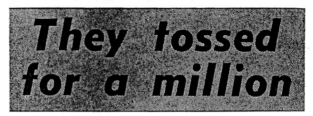

This million-dollar sidelight to the Massey-Harris and Ferguson merger was related by Harry Ferguson:

At one stage, negotiations were in danger of breaking down owing to a difference over a million dollars which neither party could concede without embarrassment to themselves and others whom they represented. I suggested a way out of the difficulty.

Turning to Colonel Phillips, the Massey-Harris executive, I said:

"Colonel, there's only one way to prevent these negotiations from breaking down and to avoid embarrassment to anyone.

"You are an Irishman. I am another. Let us be sporting and toss for it.

"If I win it will cost you a million dollars and if you win it will cost me a million; but it won't be of any consequence to anyone as the assets of our companies are being united."

Everyone laughed heartily at the suggestion and immediately accepted it as the best way out of the deadlock. Colonel Phillips then produced a half-crown and I said:

"I want to tell you before it is tossed that I know I will lose. I never win a bet of this kind."

The coin was tossed, Massey-Harris won and everyone was delighted at such a happy and complete settlement of the problem.

I then said: "Now let's toss for the fateful half-crown; I'm sure to win this kind of wager."

Yes, I won!

The famous coin later was mounted in a glass case by the Massey-Harris people.

Reasons for Amalgamation from Ferguson's Point of View Prepared and Presented by James Duncan to the UK Treasury August 13th, 1953

- Continuity of Management and development of the Ferguson plan for agricultural development so that it can be carried on after Mr Harry Ferguson is no longer able to manage the business himself
- To strengthen his selling organisation to meet problems:
  - in U.S.A. where organisation is weak
  - in Canada where it is relatively small
  - in Latin America and other export markets
  - in U.K. where an amalgamation would strengthen our hold on the U.K. market
  - This amalgamation would therefore undoubtedly result in larger exports for Britain and especially to the dollar markets of U.S.A. and Canada

To produce more food more cheaply

To bring a better standard of living to the world

Two Great World-Wide Organizations Unite

MASSEY M-H HARRIS

AND

Ferguson

Massey-Harris, pioneer in the farm implement industry, pioneer in power-farming equipment and world-leader in the self-propelled combine, now becomes greater than ever by the acquisition of Ferguson—pioneer in the application of hydraulics and the mounting of implements to make tractor and implement an integral unit—known universally as The Ferguson System, which has been much imitated but never duplicated.

From the pooling of engineering skills, the more advantageous use of manufacturing facilities and efficiency that can be effected under a single management, the new organization of Massey-Harris-Ferguson goes forward to make a greater contribution than ever by developing new and more efficient machines to make farming easier and more profitable.

The Company will continue to market the two lines separately under their well-known trade names: "Massey-Harris" and "Ferguson"

MASSEY - HARRIS - FERGUSON LIMITED

MACLEAN'S MAGAZINE, APRIL 15, 1954

Announcing the merger in "Macleans Magazine" April 1954 and the commitment to maintaining the separate Ferguson and M-H lines.

- the two organisations are complimentary rather than competitive, Ferguson being very strong in the tractor field and Massey-Harris very strong in the combine field
- the bringing into production of the new large tractor to be built in Coventry which will be sold in large quantities in all markets but will be especially suited to the North American and Canadian markets. It is felt that this association will greatly increase exports from the U.K. to these dollar markets and this aspect of the situation will be given wide publicity in our joint announcement

The Deal

Massey-Harris achieved total control of Ferguson's interests for 1,805,000 M-H shares (making him the biggest shareholder) plus 15,000,000 US dollars at an exchange rate of about 8.31 USD = £1.

Harry Ferguson became Chairman of the new company with James Duncan as President. Duncan thereby held the senior position.

Importantly M-H had acquired Ferguson's

engineering development facility at Fletchamsted Highway, Coventry ("The Fletch") but Harry Ferguson Research Ltd. was not included in the deal. This went on to develop, amongst other innovations, Ferguson's four wheel drive concepts for cars.

Announcing the Amalgamation

On 14th August, 1953 approval was finally gained for press releases to the public. M-H dealers in North America were apparently advised that same day and Ferguson dealers in North America received notifications on the 16th. However the official press release was apparently prepared on August 16th and released on the 17th.

Duncan and Ferguson went on to make speeches and statements. Here are a few key extracts from their statements:

By Harry Ferguson

- I am very glad and proud to become a partner with the great Massey-Harris organisation
- Some thirteen years ago the world was startled to hear that, for the first time in his life, the late and great Henry Ford had taken a partner. This partnership launched the now world-famous Ferguson System
- The fact that the Ferguson is the world's most imitated product today is evidence of its success
- Many people thought that the Ferguson System was the ultimate innovation in design although I have constantly stated that it was only the beginning of what must be done for the farmers of the world........
- ...... Our engineers and inventors ..... have not ceased to invent and develop in the greatest secrecy the new machines which the free world must have .....
- ...... the Ferguson Companies had had many offers of partnerships or amalgamation ..... but none were of interest ..... however Mr. Duncan, the brilliant and genial head of Massey-Harris Co. .... we were immediately attracted to each other
- After only one afternoon of demonstrating these (M-H) experts were so deeply impressed with what these new machines could do for the world ..... (Duncan summoned his co-directors and lawyers in Canada and the US and brought them over at a day's notice). Demonstrations were then carried on at full speed and heavy tractors of all makes

Harry G. Ferguson, head of the Ferguson group of companies, and James S Duncan, President of Massey-Harris sign the agreement for one of the greatest mergers in the history of agricultural machinery. This was the official photo released to the Press

were put into competition with the Ferguson

- One of the most important clauses of the agreement as far as I am concerned provides that the designs, strategy, objects and all the ideals of the Ferguson in agriculture throughout the world will be carried on with the utmost energy

By James Duncan

- The most delicate period in this amalgamation will be the first six months
- We must not forget that the difficult role will be that of Ferguson because it is they who have been absorbed
- We must understand that there is no intention on our part to absorb the Ferguson organisation by placing our management in charge of their business - or our dealers being given their representation
- .... this amalgamation must take the form of joining forces, of true partnership, and not of absorption
- One thing is sure, namely, that we are facing the biggest managerial challenge we have ever been called upon to handle
- ..... each one of us must be big enough to be unconcerned about his personal situation .... I have led off by giving up my Chairmanship of our board which is one of the most honourable positions either in Canada or the implement industry

By James Duncan to Harry Ferguson U.K. Employees

- Grateful to Mr. A. Botwood (Managing Director of Harry Ferguson Ltd.) for the privilege of meeting you all
- Congratulations on splendid work accomplished by you all under leadership of H. Ferguson and Botwood since 1946
- Just as you have pioneered in the tractors and mounted implements – so we have in the self propelled combines
- ...... have long admired the engineering genius, basis, concept and meticulous perfectionism of your great leader Mr. Harry Ferguson ..... it has been his wish and mine that we should travel together ......
- No immediate changes are contemplated either in the inside or outside of the organisation
- .... a word concerning Harry Ferguson – our endeavour to keep his great name and the contribution he has made to agriculture nailed to the mast-head of our new company

Some Press Headlines

Massey-Harris - Ferguson Merge Their World-Wide Interests.
Mr. Harry Ferguson is chairman and Mr. James Duncan president of new joint company
(Farm Implement and Machinery Review)

Secret Revolutionary Machines Will Be Marketed by the New "Massey-Harris-Ferguson" Amalgamation.
These Will Include a Large Tractor and a Small Combined-Harvester Based on Totally Different Ideas
(Power Farming)

2 Farm Tools Concerns Consolidate
(New York Journal American)

Harry Ferguson and Massey-Harris Announce Merger Plan.
Two Big Farm Equipment Makers Would Combine by Exchange of New Massey-Harris Stock

Ferguson and Massey-Harris Firms Merged

Farm Implement Firms Merge
(New York Herald Tribune)

Ferguson to Merge with Massey-Harris
(New York Times)

FERGUSON AND MASSEY-HARRIS SEE BRIGHT FUTURE
(in house release)

MASSEY-HARRIS AND FERGUSON AGREE TO UNITE
(official press release by M-H Office of the Director of Public Relations)

Merging Tractors
(The Economist)

MASSEY-HARRIS AND FERGUSON MERGER
(Financial Times)

Massey-Harris and Ferguson Amalgamate.
World Distribution Problems Still to be Settled
(Farm Mechanization)

THE HARRY FERGUSON STORY
The Tractor Inventor and Crusader who Joined Forces with a
Canadian Farm Machinery Company did so because he found a man who
Shared his Larger Ideals
(The Star Weekly, Toronto)

Above: Coming together! A Ferguson Tractor with an M-H 720 Drill. A farmyard scene painted by the celebrated artist Terence Cuneo who was retained by M-H-F to produce a series of similar oil paintings – all now very valuable.

Left: Ferguson now manufactured by Massey-Harris-Ferguson. A North American serial number plate.

The Company Officers and Management

The Top Men in Massey-Harris and Ferguson Before the Merger

Names of past company officers are frequently referred to in discussions amongst vintage machinery enthusiasts and historians, but frequently there is confusion about their origins and roles. The following short summaries are provided as guidance to how the company management evolved through the merger period.

Company officials before the merger

Massey-Harris*		Harry Ferguson Ltd. Coventry**	
Directors		Allan Botwood	Managing Director
H.H. Bloom		Eric Young	Director of Sales
G.P.Campbell Q.C.		L.G. Reid	Director of Engineering
H.J. Carmichael		Ian Wallace	Director of Co-ordination
J.S. Duncan	Chairman	E.J. Davies	Secretary
C.L. Gundy		Trevor Knox	Manager – Home Sales
H.B. Housser		Arthur Whiteley	Manager – Export Sales
G.C. Leitch		John Chambers	Chief Engineer
M.W. McCutcheon Q.C.		Alexander Senkowski	Tractor Engineer
J.A.McDougland		L.E. Summerfield	Implement Engineer
W.H. Moore Q.C.		J.Wilson	Patent Engineer and Advisor
W.E. Phillips		**Harry Ferguson Holding Ltd****	
J.A. Simard		Trevor Garbett	Private Secretary
E.P.Taylor		John R Peacock	Secretary of Holding
J.S.D Tory Q.C.		**Harry Ferguson Inc. Detroit****	
C.W.Webster		*Directors:*	
Officers		Harry G. Ferguson	Chairman
J.S. Duncan	Chairman of Board and President	Mrs Maureen Ferguson	Herman G. Klemm
H.H. Bloom	1st VP. President USA Divn.	Mrs Elizabeth M. Sheldon	Robert G. Surridge
C.N.Appleton	VP and Secretary	Horace D'Angelo	Albert A.Thornbrough
G.T.M. Bevan	VP. Dir Eng, European Divn.	Marion S. Harlan	
E.G. Burgess	VP. GM Candian Divn	*Officers and Executives*	
W. Lattman	VP. GM European Divn.	Harry G. Ferguson	President
W.W. Mahwhinney	VP. GM Export Divn.	Horace D'Angelo	Executive VP and G. Manager
R.H. Metcalfe	VP. General Administration	Herman G. Klemm	VP and Chief Engineer
M.F.Verity	VP	Robert G. Surridge	VP, G. Counsel and Sec
		Albert A Thornbrough	VP and Treasurer
		Nils Lou	VP and Tractor Plant Manager
		Curry W. Stoup	General Sales Manager
		Martin E. Fellwock	Asst. Sec. and Asst.Treasurer
		William M.Alexander	Asst. Secretary

* from 1953 annual report ** from company papers *** from1950 annual report

The Top Men at Massey-Harris-Ferguson After the Merger in 1953

(highlighted names are former Ferguson men and show how Ferguson influence was soon diluted)

Three Ferguson men were added to the old Massey-Harris board, or became officers of the new company. The new board was therefore very heavily dominated by Massey-Harris men. Harry Ferguson had only carried with him **E.W.Young** (former director of sales) and **H.G. Klemm** (former USA Chief Engineer). U.K engineering therefore advanced no representation to the new board other than through **Harry Ferguson** himself.

The First Directors and Officers of Massey-Harris-Ferguson*

The Directors	Officers	
H.G. Ferguson (Chairman)	J.S. Duncan	President
H.H. Bloom	H.H. Bloom	1st VP and President USA Division
G.P. Campbell	C.N. Appleton	VP and Secretary
H.J. Carmichael	G.T.M. Bevan	VP. Dir M-H Engineering Eastern Hemisphere Divn.
J.S. Duncan (President)	E.G. Burgess	VP. Manufacturing and Engineering. GM Canadian Divn.
C.L. Gundy	W. Lattman	VP. Planning and Procurement
H.B. Housser	W.W. Mawhinney	VP. GM Eastern Hemisphere Export Divn.
H.G. Klemm	R.H. Metcalfe	VP. General Administration
G.C. Leitch	M.F. Verity	VP
M.W. McCutcheon	**E.W. Young**	VP. MD, Eastern Hemisphere Divn.
J.A. McDougland		
W.H. Moore		
W.E. Phillips (C'man Exec Comm)		
J.A. Simmard		
E.P. Taylor		
J.S.D. Tory		
C.W. Webster		
E.W. Young		

* from 1953 annual report

The merger received Royal approval.

Even the merchandising came to reflect the new ownership – two matchbox covers of the period.

Machine castings had to change too! Two wheel weights thought to be from an M-H 735 Combine.

The 1954 annual report shows Harry Ferguson to have left the board; **H.G. Klemm** has become a VP and Director of Engineering for the Western Hemisphere, and another Detroit Ferguson man, **Albert A Thornbrough** has become a Vice President.

The 1955 annual report shows a different structure to the management team with distinct division into western and eastern hemisphere teams, and appointments for Europe.

Above: November 1954. M-H-F top brass visit Australia. At Sydney using a charter plane to visit a country centre in New South Wales. L-R: M. F Verity, J. S.Duncan, Stewart McKay, A. F. Crosby, W. Turner. Two Ferguson dealers at the top.

This page and opposite: Harry Ferguson left M-H-F to develop his four-wheel drive concept for both road and racing cars. Harry Ferguson can be seen observing the trials of the cross-country vehicle with his arm outstretched. Stirling Moss at the wheel of car No. 26.

From an early age Harry Ferguson had an interest in motor racing.

The 1955 Management Structure of Massey-Harris-Ferguson

Directors: J.S. Duncan (Chairman and President), W.E. Phillips, H.H. Bloom, H. Borden. G.P. Campbell, H.J. Carmichael, C.L. Gundy, H.B. Housser, *H.G. Klemm*, M.W. Mc Cutcheon, J.A. McDougald, W.H. Moore, J.A. Simard, E.P. Taylor.

Corporate Officers: J.S. Duncan, **A.A. Thornbrough**, H.H. Bloom, C.N. Appleton

Head Office and Western Hemisphere Division	
E.G. Burgess	VP Forward Planning and Production Engineering
H.G. Klemm	VP Director of Engineering Western Hemisphere Division
W. Lattman	VP Western Export and Continental European Operations
R.H. Metcalfe	VP General Administration
C.P. Milne	Exec. VP USA Company
L.T. Ritchie	VP MD Australian Companies
G.H Thomas	VP General Manager Canadian Division
M.F. Verity	VP Australian, South African, Barber machinery and Sunshine Waterloo Divisions
E. Abaroa	G.M Western Hemisphere Export Division
C.F. Herrmeyer	Financial Officer
J. Martin	Director of Public Relations
E.H. Metcalfe	Comptroller
C.B.C. Scott	Director of Personnel and Public Relations
A.M. Snider	VP and GM Sunshine Waterloo Company
L.M. Wiertz	GM Barber Machinery Division

Eastern Hemisphere Division	
E.W. Young	VP. MD Eastern Hemisphere Division
G.T.M. Bevan	VP. Director M-H Engineering Eastern Hemisphere Division
W.W. Mawhinney	VP. GM and VP Export Company
J.W. Beith	MD and President French Company
J.A. Bouillant-Linet	Asst. MD and Hon. President French Company. VP Export Company
R.A. Diez	GM German Company
L. Harper	MD U.K. Manufacturing and Sales Companies
A.W. Moffat	MD "SAFIM" and South African Company
W.B. Wedd	G.M. French-Belgian-German Division. VP Export Company

Albert Thornbrough took over from James Duncan as President of M-H-F, and then subsequently took the company forward to become Massey-Ferguson. He is seen here delivering a speech at a world-wide convention for the later formed M-F Industrial and Construction Machinery Division.

Herman Klemm, Harry Ferguson's chief design engineer, became a Director of the new M-H-F organisation and subsequently Vice-president of Engineering for the Western Hemisphere Division. He was responsible for designing the Ferguson 35 Tractors.

By the 1956 annual report **Albert A. Thornbrough** had come to be President following the retirement of James S. Duncan who had served the company for many years and been President from 1941-1956. Duncan had taken the Massey-Harris company through the war years to the merger; Thornbrough, a "Ferguson" man was to take the company on to become Massey-Ferguson. Both Thornbrough and E.W. Young were "Ferguson" men who were to serve through into the Massey-Ferguson era.

Note: Two other names which crop up frequently in merger period correspondence are Tom Carroll, M-H's world-famous combine engineer and Lionel Harper who was at M-H's Manchester factory in England

Daniel Massey and Harry Ferguson celebrated on the Massey-Ferguson Medal sponsored by the American Society of Agricultural Engineers.

Sydney airport. Dick Muspratt (see page 148), James Duncan, M. F. Verity, S. S. McKay

The M-H-F logo reproduced from the M-H-F annual report of 1955.

Mr and Mrs James Duncan arriving at Sydney airport greeted by Dick Muspratt (centre, and see page 148).

1953-1958

Reorganise!

Immediately following the merger, members of the new management team set about their business of re-organising the two companies into the new M-H-F company, analysing their assets, and pushing forward as appropriate new developments. The main issues which had to be tackled were:

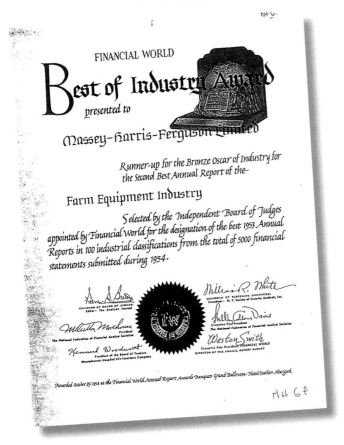

M-H-F's first Annual Report for 1953 wins a Bronze Oscar. M-H had won several awards for their annual reports even before the merger.

- sation of the management structure to bring the two companies into a working harmony
- reorganisation and rationalisation of distributor and dealership structures around the world (several documents were generated which rated their respective merits and performances)
- reassurance of dealers about how the two product lines would be retained

- reorganisation of manufacturing to include new tractors and implements
- blending of research and development activities
- production of planned new Ferguson tractors that were well past the drawing board stage. Here it is important to note that Ferguson had two different pending tractor developments on each side of the Atlantic which would both mark significant improvements on the old grey Ferguson tractors. They had to take on the already successful challenge of Ford's 8N and new Ford Jubilee in North America, as well as prove that they could displace the dated designs of the Massey-Harris tractors. Generally, power and specification improvements were overdue for all markets. In certain markets e.g. France, the small and simple Massey-Harris Pony was an on-going success.

No-one has yet explained why Harry Ferguson had decided to develop two different new tractor designs on each side of the Atlantic. However it is reported (Neufeld, 1969) that Ferguson had initially opposed the Detroit Ferguson 35 development by his engineer Klemm. Was it a matter of setting one design team against another to see which team would come up with the best solution? In the event the competition was:

Ferguson in the U.K.	Ferguson in U.S.A.
Ferguson TE 60	**Ferguson 35**
Prototype name LTX (large tractor experimental) Prototypes of 45-60 hp reported but no very specific data survives. 3-4 plough capacity but Ferguson had demonstrated with 5	(which would be the forerunner of the M-H 50, Ferguson 40 and MF 50, and lead to the higher hp MF 65) 34 hp @ 2000 rpm 3 plow capacity
Project started 1948	Natural evolution TO-20>TO-30 >TO 35

- production of new planned Ferguson side mounted implements in particular, and other Ferguson style implements
- and simple matters! Even the change of branch, distributor and dealer signs to Massey-Harris-

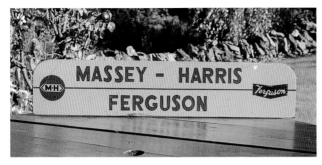

A very rare Massey-Harris and Ferguson sign.

Ferguson was to take up considerable administrative and logistical effort!

It must be noted that the merger of two companies requires the merging of their administrations and procedures to cut out duplication of effort and maybe excess resources; the merging of procurement, engineering and production procedures to bring about economies of scale, as well as bringing about a commonality of sales and marketing, service and parts supply procedures. Not an easy task given the fundamentally different nature of the two companies merging at a time of increasing competition and supply in the agricultural machinery trade. Rather like trying to merge two jigsaws into one and use fewer pieces?

The Power Base

Although the merger had been agreed and signed in the UK with M-H men travelling across the Atlantic to meet with Harry Ferguson and his team, it is important to note that as soon as it was signed the power base for the new company was to be immediately in Canada, North America - the home of Massey-Harris. Thus all major organisational and policy matters relating to the new company henceforth would mainly emanate from there.

Albert Thornbrough, a Fergsuon protégé, took over from James Duncan in 1956 and went on to resolve complex corporate problems of the fledgling M-H-F company and lead it to become Massey-Ferguson.

Above: James Duncan had the vision to exploit the market for combine harvesters in the post-war years. He resigned as President of M-H-F in 1956, partly due to ill health.

Left: Harry Ferguson ageing like James Duncan, resigned his Chairmanship of M-H-F in 1954 to pursue other engineering interests and also because of some disillusionment with the way in which M-H-F was proceeding.

General Problems Reviewed in August 1953

Problems resulting from the merger appeared to be more pronounced in North America, M-H's heartland. The following issues were reviewed there in August 1953:

- Resignation of Vice-President and tractor plant manager received
- Tractor inventory at Detroit 750. Production running at 75/day. Out shipments 45/day. Therefore bank of stock building up
- Sales ought to pick up in autumn selling season and especially if M-H dealers become interested
- Most serious problem facing Ferguson operation is the increasing inability of distributors and dealers to finance stock. They need help from a finance company or M-H-F to establish its own
- Dealers and distributors requesting higher discounts but this is not possible if to remain competitive with Ford
- Amalgamation announcement effects were determined to be:
  1. Distributors disturbed
  2. Assurance needed for them that should their distributorships be cancelled, M-H-F would

The 1954 British Ferguson Equipment Price List from M-H-F – clear evidence of the "two line" policy which was later to be abandoned.

purchase back stocks

3. Need to meet distributors and discuss the future

4. Dealers in the main are receptive to amalgamation but they need clarification of future terms and re-assurance that they will be able to buy on the same terms as for M-H equipment

Planning Project to Assure the Smoothest Possible Fusion of the Massey-Harris and Ferguson Organisation

An M-H-F planning document discussed the issues to be covered in a review of M-H and Ferguson operations in the U.S.A. and Canada. The main points were:

- For sales, the consolidation of advertising, merchandising, service and accounting was to be considered. An immediate survey of 28 Ferguson distributors in the U.S.A. and 7 in Canada to be made
- For dealer organisation it would be necessary to

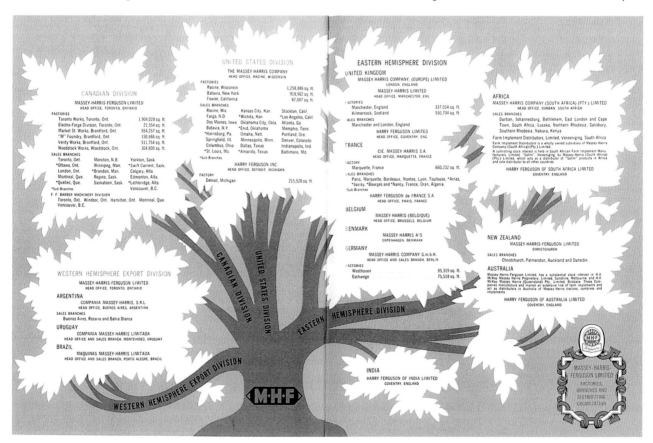

The international structure of the new M-H-F soon after the merger.

171

Ferguson   P R I C E   L I S T

TRACTOR TYPE TEF (Diesel Engine)	Ex-Works	£525 0 0
TRACTOR TYPE TEF-8 (Diesel Engine—11" Tyres)	Ex-Works	£532 10 0
TRACTOR TYPE TE-A20 (Petrol Engine)	Ex-Works	£395 0 0
TRACTOR TYPE TE-A8 (Petrol Engine—11" Tyres)	Ex-Works	£402 10 0
TRACTOR TYPE TE-D20 (Vaporising Oil Engine)	Ex-Works	£405 0 0
TRACTOR TYPE TE-D8 (V.O. Engine—11" Tyres)	Ex-Works	£412 10 0
TRACTOR TYPE TE-C20 (Narrow Track Petrol Engine)	Ex-Works	£435 0 0
TRACTOR TYPE TE-E20 (Narrow Track Vaporising Oil Engine)	Ex-Works	£445 0 0
TRACTOR TYPE TEK (Vineyard, Petrol Engine)	Ex-Works	£455 0 0
TRACTOR TYPE TEL (Vineyard, V.O. Engine)	Ex-Works	£465 0 0

Exclusive of oil surcharge of £1-8-6

BUCKRAKE		£38 0 0
Stabiliser Unit Extra		
CULTIVATORS		
RIGID TINE		£46 0 0
SPRING TINE		£46 0 0
EARTH LEVELLER		£35 0 0
Stabiliser Unit if required		£2 12 6
EARTH SCOOP		£14 10 0
MULTI-PURPOSE SEED DRILL		
Ex-Works		£157 10 0
Stabiliser Unit if required		£2 12 6
MULTI-PURPOSE SEED DRILL, with Suffolk Coulters Ex-Works		£145 0 0
FERTILISER ATTACHMENT		£72 0 0
FERTILISER ATTACHMENT (Suffolk Coulter)		£74 0 0
GAME FLUSHER		£27 10 0
HARROWS		
6' MOUNTED DISC HARROW		£84 0 0
7' MOUNTED DISC HARROW		£90 0 0
HEAVY DUTY DISC HARROW (8 disc)		£75 0 0
HEAVY DUTY DISC HARROW (10 disc)		£81 0 0
OFFSET DISC HARROW		£67 0 0
SPIKE TOOTH HARROW		£41 0 0
SPRING TOOTH HARROW 3-gang		£35 0 0
SPRING TOOTH HARROW 2-gang		£28 10 0
HIGH LIFT LOADER with Manure Fork		£112 10 0
HIGH LIFT LOADER with Bucket		£112 10 0
H/L Loader Stand if required		£4 10 0
MANURE LOADER		£55 0 0
Stabiliser Unit if required		£2 12 6
MANURE SPREADER less Hitch Ex-Works		£183 10 0
Hitch Assembly if required		£9 5 0
MOWER 5' CUTTER BAR		£82 10 0
With Stand Assembly		£84 5 0
Stabiliser Unit if required		£2 12 6
SIDE DELIVERY RAKE		£130 0 0

PLOUGHS		
PLOUGH—16" 1 FURROW (fabricated steel share)		£41 0 0
PLOUGH—16" 1 FURROW (cast iron share)		£40 0 0
2 FURROW 12" SEMI DIGGER (cast iron share)		£50 0 0
2 FURROW 12" SEMI DIGGER (steel share)		£51 0 0
2 FURROW 12" DEEP DIGGER (cast iron share)		£54 0 0
2 FURROW 10" GENERAL PURPOSE (cast iron share)		£50 0 0
2 FURROW 10" SEMI DIGGER (fabricated steel share)		£51 0 0
2 FURROW 10" SEMI DIGGER (cast iron share)		£50 0 0
3 FURROW 8"		£79 10 0
2 FURROW 10" LEA (cast iron share)		£52 0 0
3 FURROW 10" GENERAL PURPOSE (cast iron share)		£76 0 0
3 FURROW 10" SEMI DIGGER (cast iron share)		£76 0 0
3 FURROW 10" LEA (cast iron share)		£79 10 0
STANDARD 2 FURROW PLOUGH		£44 0 0
REVERSIBLE PLOUGH		£102 10 0
PLOUGH DISC 2 FURROW		£66 0 0
SUB-SOILER		£28 0 0
POST HOLE DIGGER (9" or 12" Auger)		£53 0 0
Stabiliser Unit if required		£2 12 6
POTATO PLANTER (Hopper Attachment to Ridger)		£25 10 0
Chitted Seed Tray (Attachment to Ridger)		£22 10 0
POTATO SPINNER		£84 0 0
Stabiliser Unit if required		£2 12 6
RIDGER		£43 0 0
INDEPENDENT GANG STEERAGE HOE (with discs)		£117 0 0
Less Discs		£105 0 0
SPRAYER (Low Volume)		£84 0 0
SPRAYER (Medium)		£225 0 0
Tank Filling Unit		£15 10 0
STEERAGE HOES		
with discs		£86 0 0
without discs		£65 0 0
TILLER		£49 0 0
TRANSPORT BOX		£10 10 0
TRAILERS		
3-Ton TIPPING less Hitch Ex-Works		£162 10 0
3-Ton NON-TIPPING less Hitch Ex-Works		£132 10 0
30 cwt. TIPPING TRAILER Ex-Works		£112 10 0
30 cwt. FIXED TRAILER Ex-Works		£90 0 0
Hitch Assembly if required		£9 5 0
WEEDER		£35 10 0
WINCH		£88 0 0
WOOD SAW		£34 10 0
HAMMERMILL		£107 10 0
STATIONARY HAMMERMILL		£97 10 0
REAR MOUNTED CRANE		£15 0 0

ACCESSORIES

BELT PULLEY ATTACHMENT		£14 0 0
AUTOMATIC HITCH ASSEMBLY (Used in conjunction with Trailers and Manure Spreader)		£9 5 0
STAND ASSEMBLY H/L LOADER		£4 10 0
STEEL WHEELS, OPEN TYPE 42" per pair		£35 0 0
STEEL WHEELS, 40" x 10", per pair		£31 0 0
STABILISER BRACKET ASSEMBLY		£2 12 6
HARVEST LADDERS		£10 15 0
THIRD FURROW CONVERSION SET		
(cast iron share)		£27 10 0
(fabricated steel share)		£28 5 0
TRACTOR COVER		£3 15 0
TRAILER CONVERSION SET		£34 10 0
HITCH CONVERSION UNIT		£10 15 0
TYRE INFLATOR SET		£1 5 9
UNIVERSAL COUPLING		£2 10 0

WHEEL GIRDLES, 10", per pair		£19 10 0
Less Lugs		£16 10 0
WHEEL GIRDLES, 11", per pair		£23 0 0
Less Lugs		£19 10 0
MOWER STAND		£1 15 0
DUAL WHEEL ATTACHMENT KIT		£5 5 0
WHEELBARROW CONVERSION SET		£8 0 0
FRONT WHEEL WEIGHTS, per pair		£6 10 0
JACK		£4 15 0
VINEYARD TRACTOR JACK		£4 10 0
HINGED SEAT AND FOOTREST ASSEMBLY		£3 10 0
RIDGER COVERING BODIES		£12 10 0
TRACTOR SEAT CUSHION		£2 5 0
TRACTOMETER		£11 5 0
SINGLE ARM COULTER	Price according to Model. Ask your Dealer.	
FURROW WIDTH ADJUSTER		

ALL PRICES, EXCEPT WHERE MARKED EX-WORKS, INCLUDE CARRIAGE PAID TO DEALER ON MAINLAND OR F.A.S. MAINLAND PORT, AND ARE SUBJECT TO ALTERATION WITHOUT NOTICE.

Massey-Harris-Ferguson (Sales) Limited, Coventry, England.

Printed in England.   FP/291/15000/JUNE, 1954

An American dealers' sign distinctly separating the two lines.

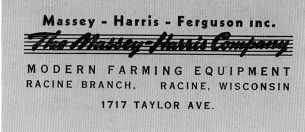

Envelope address showing Massey-Harris still as a company of M-H-F.

survey dealers first. They would need advice of whether contracts were to be M-H, Ferguson or in special cases represent both. Consideration would be given to expansion and fusion of dealer organisations

- In engineering look for duplication of equipment and make recommendations to cover the discontinuance of slow selling or obsolete machines. A review of engineering facilities was planned for 1954 that would determine the facilities required, their location and the management needed.
- For manufacturing, determine the equipment now supplied by outside manufacturers that can be manufactured in house. Arrange for production of such equipment and relevant logistical backup.
- With purchasing and procurement procedures it would be necessary to determine the degree of co-ordination and standardisation of policy required to assure procurement at the best possible prices, together with the establishment of adequate inventory control etc etc.
- In accounting the degree of accounting standardisation possible and possibilities for amalgamation of existing departments would be determined.

Great emphasis was placed on defining that a two line policy would continue as follows:

- There will continue to be Ferguson Tractors and Ferguson System Implements bearing the Ferguson name.
- There will continue to be Massey-Harris Tractors and Equipment bearing the Massey-Harris name.
- There will continue to be Dealers handling the sales and service of Ferguson Tractors and Ferguson

System Implements.
- There will continue to be Dealers handling the sales and service of Massey-Harris Tractors and Equipment.

In the Final Analysis

In the final analysis the M-H-F years were to see a rationalisation of dealerships to become ultimately MF dealerships with the dropping of the two line policy. This was to cost M-H-F dearly in terms of time and effort used up in trying to make it work, and then compensating affected dealers once it was realised that it was not a viable policy. This was most difficult in North America but was to happen worldwide. Some great battles were fought with dealers on both sides of the Atlantic!

Tractor design and production came to abandon the Massey-Harris style tractors despite the introduction of some new models in the period. The Ferguson System style of tractors was adopted for future tractor design based on the concepts developed at Detroit (the Ferguson 35) and not the new Ferguson concept LTX tractor developed in the UK (which was planned to be designated the Ferguson TE 60). In hand Ferguson developments at the time of the merger for harvesting equipment were ultimately abandoned. The side mounted combines never went into production and the side mounted balers and foragers had a short and limited commercial run; the balers being withdrawn from service and scrapped.

Summary of Tractor Model Evolution

The following table gives a listing of all the tractor models of the merger years, including ones that came with the merger, ones that appeared in the merger period and some that appeared immediately after.

Tractors of the merger period

	"Before"		Merger years				"After"
	1952	October 31st 1953	1954	1955	1956	December 1957	1958
U.K.							
Ferguson TE 20 incl. industrials	x	x	x	x	x		
Ferguson FE 35 incl. industrials					x	x	x
MF 65 (765)						Introduced	x
M-H 744	x	x	x				
M-H 745 and 745S			x	x	x	x	x
France							
FF30 (=TE-20 assembled in France)						x	x
M-H 811 Pony	x	x					
M-H 812 Pony		x	x	x	x	x	x
M-H 820 Pony						x	x
MF 835							x
Canada							
M-H Pony	x	x	x				
U.S.A. Agriculturals							
Ferguson TO 30	x	x	x				
Ferguson TO 35			x	x	x	x	x
Ferguson 40					x	x	
M-H Pony	x	x	x				
M-H Colt (21)	x	x					
M-H Pacer			x	x	x		
M-H Mustang (23)	x	x	x	x	x		
M-H 22	x						
M-H 33	x	x	x	x			
M-H 44	x	x	x #	x #			
M-H 55	x	x	x	x			
M-H 333					x	x	
M-H 444					x	x	x
M-H 555				x	x	x	x
M-H 50				x	x	x	x ##
MF 65						x	x
MF 85							x
MF 95							x
U.S.A. Industrials							
M-H I-162		x					
M-H I 330G			x				
M-H I-244				x	x	x	
M-H FSI-244				x	x		
M-H-F 303 Work Bull					x	x	x

#only the Special ##changed to MF in the year

Note 1. The first true industrial tractor in the UK came in 1959 with the MF 702, although there were industrial "versions" of the TE 20 and FE 35 tractors.

Note 2. The above "introduction" dates are derived from serial number data in the main. Actual dates of introduction to different country markets may have been different.

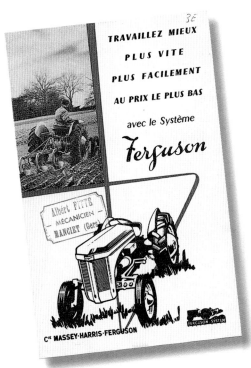

1955 French advertising for the
Ferguson Tractor by the M-H-F company.

Left to right:—Mr. H. S. Weale, production director, Standard Motor Co.; Mr. I. J. Wallace, director of supply and control, Massey-Harris-Ferguson, eastern hemisphere division; Mr. T. V. Knox, sales director Massey-Harris-Ferguson (Sales), Ltd.; Mr. A. Dick, managing director of the Standard Motor Co.; Mr. L. Harper, managing director, Massey-Harris-Ferguson (Sales), Ltd., and Massey-Harris-Ferguson (Manufacturing), Ltd.; Mr. E. Young, vice-president and managing director of Massey-Harris-Ferguson, eastern hemisphere division, and Mr. L. G. Reid, deputy director of engineering, Massey-Harris-Ferguson, eastern hemisphere division, with the half-millionth Coventry-produced " Ferguson " Tractor,

A fuller line-up of top brass for the half millionth Ferguson.

Any manufacturer's dream – half a million tractors of essentially the same model.
Alec Dick at the wheel, Eric Young standing.

The M-H 333 and 444 Tractors were two of M-H's last M-H design tractor models, the third being the larger M-H 555, produced in M-H-F days. Duane Drohman has two unique examples of these tractors as noted on his show display board. Will he find the first M-H 555?

YOU ARE LOOKING AT THE FIRST MASSEY HARRIS MODELS "333" AND "444" BUILT. THE MODELS "50", "333", "444" AND "555" ARE THE LAST SERIES OF THE MASSEY HARRIS LINE PRODUCED. THEY ARE CONSIDERED "CLASSICS" WITH THEIR BRONZE MOTORS, RED & YELLOW COLORS AND CHROME TRIM.
THE MODEL "333" S/N 333-GIRF-20001 WAS BOUGHT IN MANITOBA, CANADA ON A SEMI LOAD OF OLD TRACTORS BY CHUCK COONEY, OF WOODBINE-IOWA. IT WAS OWNED & RESTORED BY PAUL LEHMAN OF PERRY, IOWA.
THE MODEL "444" S/N 444-GIRF-70001 WAS BOUGHT FROM BERNARD SUIPRENOUT OF BEECHER, ILLINOIS. HE HAD THE HONOR OF SEEING THE NEW LINE OF MASSEY HARRIS "333" AND "444" UNVEILED AT THE FACTORY BANQUET IN RACINE, WISCONSIN IN 1956. LITTLE DID HE KNOW AT THE TIME, THAT EXACTLY 40 YEARS LATER IN 1996, HE WOULD UNKNOWINGLY BUY THAT VERY SAME "444" AT A FARM SALE IN ROCKFORD, ILLINOIS.

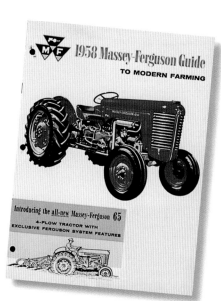

Left: One of the first M-F catalogues shows the North American style M-F 65 Tractor. Even in this start of the M-F era MF 35, 50 and 65 Tractors featured along with the last M-H Tractors – the M-H 333, 444 and 555s. Stocks of these had still to be sold out. M-F had yet to get into higher horsepower tractors with the Ferguson System to replace these heavy M-H lugging tractors which were so favoured in the big grain growing areas.

Right: Treble badging for this M-H 444 Tractor! The M-H 333, 444, and 555 Tractor were the last of the old M-H style tractors.

Above: The M-H 75 Tractor was only ever made as a prototype. It was designed as a higher power version of the M-H 50 and is clearly a Ferguson style tractor.

Right: A Ferguson TO-30 Tractor which succeeded the TO-20 in North America.

A restored Ferguson 40 Tractor. This was first made as the M-H 50 Tractor (different tin work and colours) to satisfy North American M-H dealers' need for a Ferguson type tractor. Subsequently it became the M-F 50 Tractor which had the M-H styling and new M-F red and grey colours.

An M-H-F 404 Industrial Tractor based on the agricultural M-H 444 Tractor.

Below left: The M-H Pony Tractor was painted grey for Ferguson dealers in North America to help clear stocks. It was known as the Ferguson Pony Tractor. A normal red M-H Pony can be seen to the rear of the grey Ferguson Pony.

Below: Full evidence of the conversion of the M-H Pony Tractor to a Ferguson Pony. What would Harry Ferguson have said?

Combine Harvesters and Balers

The following table gives an indication of how the combine and baler range developed over the merger period. The Ferguson side mounted combines never reached commercial production. The side mounted baler was produced in limited numbers but was withdrawn from service.

Combine Harvesters and Balers of the merger period

	1952	1953	1954	1955	1956	1957	1958
North America Combines							
15 and 17 PT and SP Canada	x	x					
26 SP Canada	x						
27 SP Canada	x						
35 SP							x
Clipper PT USA	x						
Clipper SP USA	x	x					
50 Clipper PT USA	x	x	x	x	x	x	x
60 SP Canada	x	x	x	x	x	x	x
60 PT Canada	x	x	x	x	x	x	x
70 SP Canada		x					
80 SP Canada?	x	x	x	x	x		
82 SP Canada						x	x
90 SP Canada?		x	x	x	x		
92 SP Canada						x	x
Self Propelled Picker		?	?	?	?	x	x
Corn Picker two row mounted			?	?	?	?	x
MF 4 Corn Picker trailed.							x
U.K. Combines							
726	x	x					
735					x	x	x
750	x	x	x	x	x		
780		x	x	x	x	x	x
Australia Combines							
585							
H.V.McKay machines	?	?	?	?	?	?	
Germany Combines							
630			x	x	x	x	x
685						x	x
780			?	?	?	?	
890			?	?	?	?	
France Combines							
890		x	x	x	x	x	x
830							x
France pick up press							x
North American Balers							
No 1 pull type	x	x	x	x	x	x	
No 3 pull type					x	x	x
Ferguson 12 pull type						x	x
Ferguson side mounted				x	x		
UK Balers							
701	x	x	x	x	x	x	x
703						x	x

? = uncertain records

A classic shot of the "marriage". A Ferguson Tractor pulling an M-H 701 Baler.

A Happy M-H-F Christmas to all. From the front cover of the Farmer and Stockbreeder 1955

Perhaps the last ever Ferguson calendar? Inside, an implement or tractor was featured for each month and included the Ferguson 40 Tractor together with the Ferguson Side-mounted Baler and Forage Harvester.

In Summary –

The main results of manoeuvrings within M-H-F that went on during the merger years were:

• Tractor and implement development and production adopted the Ferguson System – logical given that M-H had bought Ferguson for the Ferguson System, its world-beating tractors and implements

• Harvesting machinery development and production followed established and world-beating designs – logical given that harvesting machinery and not tractors were M-H's real strength at the time of the merger

• The unmanageable two line policy was abandoned and the dealership network rationalised. A single product line was adopted in 1957

• Harry Ferguson resigned from the company in 1954 in some large measure due to the new M-H-F company not adopting the LTX tractor (yet the Ferguson 35 tractor which replaced it was also the alternative Ferguson design tractor developed under Harry Ferguson's management). The LTX tractor was officially dropped at a company conference on mainly technical development matters held in San Antonio in March 1954

• James Duncan resigned in 1956 due to pressure from within the company and poor health

• A A Thornbrough became the new President of the company after James Duncan and he came to oversee the discontinuation of the M-H tractor line by the end of the M-H-F period

• At the end of the M-H-F period the name was changed officially to Massey-Ferguson in late 1957 and the company became publicly known as this from spring 1958 onwards. Some years later the hyphen in M-F was dropped

• The stage had been set for the development of one of the world's top agricultural equipment companies.

There can be no doubt that the merger occurred at a time when Ferguson's business in North America had hit hard times due to increasing competition, particularly from Ford. James Duncan advised Harry Ferguson that the Ferguson side of the M-H-F business lost a lot of money in 1954 and was likely to do so again in 1955. In 1954 James Duncan commented in a memo to Herman Klemm, previously Harry Ferguson's chief engineer in Detroit and by then M-H-F's chief engineer for North America, as follows:

• "With regards to blending in the expertise of the Ferguson engineers:

.... *I must be frank in admitting that my most serious anxiety in connection with the engineering divisions on both sides of the Atlantic is that the ex-Ferguson men, upon whom we are relying so heavily, are insufficiently price conscious.*

.... *They have all been trained in a school which was based upon a design which was dissimilar to that of anything on the market, and therefore not subject to normal competitive factors and where the profit element was looked upon as of minor importance, considering that no capital expenditures were made and very little working capital required.*

(Note: Ferguson had only ever had to fund the one factory in Detroit which really was an assembly plant rather than true manufacturing plant status)

• With regards to market prospects:

..... *Today the Ferguson concept is copied everywhere. The implements and tractors are sold on extended terms, and unlike the 1939-1943 period of shortages, the supply is now greater than the demand and sales are largely governed by consideration of terms and price.*

The situation is, therefore, radically changed in the western hemisphere and will be changed in the eastern hemisphere just as soon as competition from Ford and others makes itself felt.

• Unification of engineering efforts and practices:

...... *whereas I believe that the company's best interest will ultimately be served by a complete co-ordination of all engineering on a world-wide scale, I believe that such a move before the co-ordination of North American engineering has been effected and working smoothly would be premature*

...... *world-wide interchangeability of parts desirable"*

Perhaps these are some of the most profound comments to come out of the merger period? Maybe they give much rationale as to how the M-H-F and ultimately M-F business and technological development were going to unfurl?

Ferguson's Detroit Tractor Plant was expanded in early M-F days to evolve to become the M-F "Tractor Plant and Engineering" and was commonly known as the "Southfield Road" Plant. The new building at the right rear was for manufacture of the massive articulated M-F Four Wheel Drive Tractors.

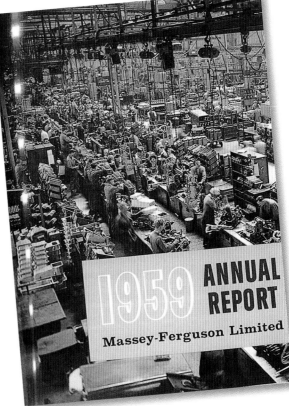

A hive of activity in 1959 at the M-F Detroit Tractor Plant, previously Harry Ferguson's Ferguson Tractor Plant

THE MEMORIES

No matter how much one consults official literature, nothing can bring to light the human nature of the Massey-Harris-Ferguson period as well as the memories of those who worked for the company or had some involvement with their products. I invited a considerable number of ex-employees, and others associated with the company, to contribute to this chapter. This they did by either their own individually written contributions, or my interviewing them in person or on the telephone. I asked them to focus on the 1953-1958 period, but indicated that some considerable latitude either side of this date was acceptable in order that their memories of the merger period would be in the context of the "Foundations of Massey Ferguson".

The contributions are a unique record of their work and the times. For convenience I have arranged them in alphabetical name order except for the first three who were so close to Mr Ferguson. I am very grateful to them and the efforts they made to facilitate this chapter; they have made a significant contribution to the human history and spirit of the time. As an outsider, I was immensely impressed by the degree of camaraderie that existed, not withstanding the natural rivalries between the "red" and "grey" men at the time. It is noted that some of the contributors were almost, or over, 90 years old. They made profuse apologies for their memories! So there may be odd facts that are not absolutely accurate, but the general gist of their stories is quite correct. Sadly several of the contributors are no longer with us – I am deeply indebted to them for their help which was given so generously and so enthusiastically.

Mr Ferguson's Personal Private Assistant (UK)

Mr Anthony Sheldon

Harry Ferguson's daughter and I had been married for about a year when he kindly offered me a job as his personal private assistant. As I was in not too good a job I was very glad to accept as it was a most interesting operation. Basically I would drive his very nice Rolls Royce to Coventry and back and probably to London and back and do all the normal things that a personal assistant is meant to do. Consequently I met all the directors of Harry Ferguson Limited and the American company.

The English company was run by Alan Bottwood which was really a marketing operation as the tractors were made by the Standard Motor Company in volume and the implements were individually manufactured by various manufacturers such as Rubery Owen, round Britain. The whole Ferguson concept reformed the tractor industry, with its hydraulic linkage, depth control and safety systems. It was a revolution. I was able to understand and help.

When I got into the job properly I found that he was working on a larger version of the Fergie tractor and also with Tony Rolt and Freddie Dixon on a four wheel drive anti-skid braking motor car. All of which I found completely fascinating and was involved. As a result of all this there was plenty to do and we were very busy.

He had been having medical treatment, this was getting more frequent and he wasn't feeling at all bright at times and I think he felt he couldn't cope with the intensity of the work required in the future so he started looking round for a partner.

In his travels he had met Mr James Duncan who was the Chairman of the Massey Harris Company and they produced a wide range of implements and so fitted neatly in to the Ferguson plan. He was advised at this time by a chartered accountant, John

Turner and a lawyer and they laid the plans for the amalgamation of the two companies. This solved his problem because he felt he was not well enough to carry on at the intensity required. It has turned out his prediction for four wheel drive systems for motor cars is now at last in 2003 beginning to come true.

Abbotswood, his home, was the most wonderful place with its gardens and staff to entertain any directors from overseas etc, and so the two sides got together and agreed everything, except at the last moment there was a million dollars difference between them and Harry said, "Let's toss for it" and they tossed for it and he lost and they had the coin inlaid in the most wonderful silver cigar box and presented it to him.

Diesel course of Instruction, No. 72 - 23rd-27th July, 1951
Seated, Left to Right - J.Berkeley, J.Davitt, K. Ham, W. A. Clayton, H.G. Rumford, **A. Sheldon**, R. Broad, H. W. Jeffrey, H. Pearson, R.E. Weale, J. Smith
Standing, Left to Right - J. Miles, J. Genus, P. M. Franklin, M. Medart, Mrs. U. Bryant, A. N. Douse, D. B. Purchas, W. B. Lightwing, J. Tilleman, J. de R'jke, M. Braggiotti, V. Hogan.

Anthony Sheldon's father-in-law Harry Ferguson mowing the estate at Abbotswood.

A Quick Appointment (UK, USA)

Sir Ian Wallace

Now in my mid 80s my mental picture of early contact with Harry Ferguson Ltd. is very vivid but information on precise dates somewhat suspect!

At a small private cocktail party in the Savoy Hotel, I met that most impressive character Roger Kyes in late autumn of 1947. He explained that he was involved in the development of agricultural mechanisation under a new system, the inventor of which was present, and suggested that I meet him. My first contact there and then was a brief handshake with Mr Harry Ferguson who just spent a minute or two listening to my response to his enquiry – "What do you do?" Another handshake and away, with Roger Kyes who asked me to join him for dinner. After dinner he said, "Young man, I have been ringing the bells on you and have concluded that you are wasting your time at Lloyd's; I think you should come and join us."

I took no immediate action but about a fortnight later a telephone call from Mr Kyes – "Young man, I told you that you were wasting your time at Lloyd's and suggested you joined us, but I have never heard anything more from you." To this I replied, "Yes I remember our meeting and your suggestion that I was wasting my time but you didn't indicate how much." There and then he made me an offer which was just too good to miss. His salary offer was three times that which I was earning in the Under-writing Room at Lloyd's and his suggestion was that myself and family all go first class on the Queen Mary with a suite in the best hotel in Detroit – at that time the Book Cadillac.

"What we want you to do is to learn all about our business and how we work with Ford Motor Company." I jumped at the opportunity naturally; I don't think there was anything in writing; it was all a verbal arrangement and we were off on the next sailing of the Queen Mary. That is how it started.

For the next month or two, living in the Book Cadillac Hotel, Washington Boulevard, Detroit I travelled daily back and forth along Woodward Avenue to Ford Dearborn where I found Harry Ferguson Limited office on the first floor of the Ford 'H' building.

My first and most important contact was with Mr Albert Thornbrough who was one of the top executives of Mr Ferguson's American Company. He was so very kind inviting me out to his home where I spent several most memorable evenings with him and his wife, watching television etc.

During the day of course, it was the other executives in Mr Ferguson's company who were so good to me, showing me all the background information papers, price structures, methods of delivery to distributors and of course the production arrangements for all the implements that were a vital integral part of the Ferguson system.

Then one day came the bombshell! Without any warning Ford Motor would cease producing tractors for us and there we were without a prime mover and commitments (all out on contracts) of millions of dollars, for the range of implements that made up the Ferguson system!

In the afternoon I had a call – would I go down and meet Mr Ferguson and join him in his car and drive back to the hotel where we were both staying? On our arrival at the hotel Mr Ferguson said, "Well what are you going to do now?" and I replied that having attended a demonstration of the Ferguson System in a tent one day at Coventry I had been so enthusiastic for the system and its potentiality that I had decided to leave Lloyd's and so I just didn't know what I was going to do now.

The following day an executive from Mr Ferguson's company met with me at the hotel and told me that I was to go back to Britain and be Personal Assistant to the Managing Director of the Ferguson Company in Coventry.

Back at Coventry, I found Harry Ferguson Limited was in a small suite of offices over what had been the showroom of the Standard Motor company at Fletchamstead Highway.

I walked along the passage and was about to knock on the door of the Managing Director's office when another man (an American whose name I found was Graham Trainor) came up and asked me what I was doing there. I informed him that I had been appointed to be Personal Assistant to the Managing Director of

Harry Ferguson Ltd. "Oh! Chuck Vincent; he has a hangover and won't be in today! It was Cheltenham Races yesterday you know. Come back tomorrow."

It did not take Harry Ferguson long to clear up that situation and I was happy to meet Mr Alan Botwood the new appointee who had just arrived to take over the Managing Directorship of Harry Ferguson Limited. There I met Mr Ferguson again and learned that he wished me to join the Board but he was not prepared to offer me any shares in the Company.

In those first few days I met Bill Reed, Eric Young and John Peacock, the Secretary of the Company (almost immediately to be replaced by Eric Davies. John Peacock continued to be the close private secretary of Mr Ferguson and operated at his home – Abbotswood, Stow-on-the Wold).

My first two main tasks were:

(i) Procure a source for partitioning to make the range of offices there at Fletchamstead. A serious problem in those days because all materials were on licence. Botwood told me to go away and get this problem licked or he didn't want to see me again! – or words to that effect.

Thank Heaven I met Raymond Brookes, a senior executive and Managing Director of Garringtons, the drop forging plant of GKN. I explained our predicament – large open floor space; no licences available – could he possibly do something to help? This he most certainly did, undertaking to provide all the partitioning to make the offices we required out of the showroom and manufacturing area at Standard Motor Company's Fletchamstead premises.

The first few offices up, we had a visit from a Ministry civil servant regarding our further requirements and I was shocked when he asked how we got the licence for the room we were now in, which of course I hadn't got. Great relief to learn that the partitions were in obscured glass and therefore free of duty. It was that type of construction which we used for all our offices in the large floor area at Fletchamstead.

Brookes must have known that the type of partitioning was free of licence and knowing that the GKN Group were behind our operation, had no further trouble at all from Ministry interference. Special tribute must be paid to the Guest Keen Nettlefold organisation as a whole, who incurred enormous capital expenditure building Garringtons and Sankey Sheldon as our requirements exceeded

Alex Patterson (left, and see page 147), who had been Harry Ferguson's (then M-H-F and M-F) Engineering Superintendent on his last day at work for M-F with Sir Ian Wallace

the total capacity of the drop forging industry at that time, and Sankey Sheldon for all the partitioning. All this was achieved with remarkable pace – everybody knowing that Raymond Brookes and GKN were behind the project!

(ii) My next task was to find an agricultural property that could be used to develop our training school. The first choice was that of the Earl of Aylesford – Packington Park. When it came to taking over areas of land for our training purposes, the elderly Earl did prove to be very difficult to get on with and future relationships were not propitious. Everywhere I went I was frustrated by Ministry of Agriculture opposition because of the vital need to keep every acre in food production. I then had the good fortune to meet Robin, Lord Leigh of Stoneleigh Abbey, and on behalf of the Company, a verbal agreement was made.

We would bring into cultivation 150 acres at a time (which had never been cultivated) and in return we would undertake the reconstruction and strengthening of that wonderful 15th Century Undercroft at the Abbey. (I am told one of the finest in Britain which at that time was full of coal, coke and rubbish!) This satisfied everybody. The Ministry could not complain because in 250 years the Park had never been other than a deer park and Robin Leigh could never afford the job we undertook to tackle in the Undercroft. This incidentally, proved to be a very expensive undertaking as we had to shore up the whole Abbey to remove and construct new hexagonally cut stone pillars. If anybody goes there today I am sure they will admire what we did.

As I cast my mind over these very earliest days of the development of Harry Ferguson Limited, I would suspect that I am today certainly, the oldest living executive who had direct personal contact and involvement in the development of the production facilities for the tractors and essential matching earth engaging implements that constituted the Ferguson system, which, it should be repeated, was the unique invention of Harry Ferguson, involving as it did transferring the operative weight of the tractor as the earth engaging suck of plough and other implements, increased.

H V McKay

Everything seemed to be going world-wide on the merger OK but apparently somebody in the Massey-Harris organisation years ago had agreed, I think, that in perpetuity as long as Massey-Harris were operating in Australia, the name Massey-Harris would be linked to H V McKay and so the company in Australia had been H V McKay Massey-Harris-Ferguson. What could we do? We had to buy them out. I think it may have been three or four million pounds to buy them out and buy the factory. That enabled them for the first time to call themselves Massey-Harris-Ferguson. Having got rid of the McKay brothers, they could then drop the Harris and be Massey-Ferguson.

We had a stand at the first Smithfield Show after the merger and Prince Phillip came over to talk to Lionel Harper, the UK Director. He asked "What's 'appened to Mr 'arris?" Lionel Harper had no idea what he was talking about. Prince Phillip repeated the question, chuckled and walked away. (Mr Harris was a character in a Charles Dickens' novel and was well known for dropping his 'h's'.)

On the merger – Lionel Harper was UK Managing Director for Massey-Harris. He came to my office with James Duncan with a big map of the UK and Ireland and said, "Now look at these marks. Harry Ferguson dealers, about 150, and here's Massey Harris with 700 dealers." Most were nothing but ironmongers, not really dealers. I turned to Lionel Harper and

Stoneleigh Abbey. Site of the first Ferguson School of Farm Mechanisation. This old framed photo used to hang by the Director's office.

said, "Sheer numbers of so-called dealers are not any indication of strength. Does every one have a van and provide full service, and make a profit from it? Until they make a profit, you'll get nowhere." This type of thing was typical of the difference between Massey-Harris and Harry Ferguson.

I had lunch with Colonel Phillips, James Duncan and E. P. Taylor (a multi-millionaire from Canada Brewers), one of three in the Argos Corporation who had bought Harry Ferguson Ltd. After lunch at Claridges we walked to the Standard Motor Company office in Berkeley Square. There we made a formal announcement released to the press that we were buying the Standard Motor Company. Britain at that time was very short of foreign exchange and they didn't think they were getting enough Massey-Harris value – paying too much in shares and not getting enough cash. The deal fell through after a few weeks. The idea had been that Billy Roots of Roots would take over the Standard Motor Company car production and hand over Banner Lane to Massey-Ferguson.

M-F bought Standard Motor Co.'s works at Banner Lane where Ferguson Tractors had been made for Harry Ferguson and then M-H-F. It was bought in 1959 and subsequently closed in 2004 and demolished in 2005. On October 15th,1996 it produced its three millionth tractor.

The three millionth tractor being blessed at Coventry Cathedral.

Looking After the Estate (UK)

Peter Warr

I worked with Mr Ferguson as Estate Foreman from July 1950 until his death in 1960 and still work for the Ferguson family to this day.

I first heard of the Merger the day before it was released to the press. Mr. Ferguson told me of the Merger and that we would be having demonstrations of the LTX tractors at Abbotswood very soon. I had the privilege to drive these beautiful tractors and was very, very impressed.

Despite all this excitement I saw Mr Ferguson twice a day as usual, when he came round the estate. He would enquire how the work was progressing and if I wanted him to make any decisions. He was very cheerful and in high spirits over the Merger. He said it was ideal for both Companies, as Ferguson were world leaders in tractor design technology and Massey-Harris were leaders in the harvesting field with their machinery.

He said that the merger would benefit the whole world, as it would enable food to be produced and harvested more economically so that third world countries where starvation was a major problem would be fed.

This would give Mr Ferguson what he had striven for all his life – cheaper food for the world.

Despite all the goings on with the Merger Mr Ferguson still found time to test new tractor modifications and implements in the Park at Abbotswood, and to this day I can still see him driving round the park on his greatly loved TED 20 mowing in the summer and rolling with a ring roller in the winter.

A small Ferguson prototype tractor at work.

The survivor from the golf course.

Peter was well aware of Harry Ferguson's programme to develop a new small tractor after his departure from M-H-F. This is a mock up of the tractor made at Harry Ferguson's Tractor Research Ltd. Several prototypes were made and one went to work on Harry Ferguson's Abbotswood Estate under Peter for many years, then was subsequently loaned to Bourton on the Water Cricket Club. Another LPG (butane) tractor survives in Scotland. Sadly Harry Ferguson died in 1960 and a new commercial Ferguson small tractor never came to fruition. (Courtesy of Frank Inns)

Harry Ferguson cleaning a stream bank on his estate

In India at the Time (India, UK)

John Armstrong

Introducing the "grey-gold" Ferguson 35 tractor in India.

John Armstrong spent ten years in India with the Harry Ferguson organisation and its distributors and dealers. He later became a regional manager for MF over Scotland and Northern Ireland. Before going to India he was an instructor at the Ferguson Training Centre. He was in India at the time of the merger and reports that it had very little effect on them. Massey-Harris only had two outlets there, and their staff mostly came over to Ferguson. M-H was marketing the 744 and 745 tractors which apparently suffered a lot of broken crankshafts due, he thinks, to poor maintenance rather than poor design. At the time he was in India, Ferguson had 80% of tractor sales, but loss of the Escort distributor led this company to go off and build competitor tractors, and now they sell more than TAFE (who manufacture MF products under licence).

John recalls the excellent performance of the LTX tractor in many demonstrations, how it had single lever hydraulics and the top link was two way acting, unlike the TE-20 tractor which was only active in one direction. He described the hydraulic system as being very sensitive. It was also more robust than that of the TE-20, but of the same basic design. John stated that despite these features, visiting M-H men from North America apparently failed to be impressed by it. When I discussed with him possible reasons for the ultimate rejection of the tractor in favour of the FE-35 concept he thought there were possibly four reasons – internal company politics, a good engine but not immediately available in commercial numbers, the transmission housing was very difficult to manufacture, and the FE-35 had incorporated the universal parts concept. So it appears that these three technical reasons and politics caused one Ferguson tractor concept to kill off another!

Workshop Projects and Scrapping Prototypes (UK)

"Hammie" (Hamilton) T. Baird

Hammie Baird demonstrating an MF 788 Combine fitted with a draper header at Mauchlene in Scotland, 1958.

Hammie joined M-H-F at Kilmarnock in 1957, being appointed on March 27th but having to wait until the National Strike ended to take up his position as a fitter. The pay was 5s 6½d. per hour. He subsequently transferred to M-F at Coventry in 1960. Throughout his working life he has been widely involved in safety at the company as the representative for the Amalgamated Electrical and Engineering Union. In retirement he acted as an official guide for visitors to the Banner Lane factory, so many who read this book will recall his factory tours.

The workforce in the "Engineering Workshop" was of many skills and trades, and many different types of machines were made, modified and tested. Below are some of the projects that were worked on and, I hope!, in the order by year they were undertaken from 1957 onwards. Essentially these were the types of projects being undertaken when M-F was in its formative years.

Both the M-H 744 D Tractor and M-H 701 Baler were made at Kilmarnock.

Kilmarnock 1957-1960

735 combine - chain drives for elevators, straw walkers and the reel - not introduced

Draper pick-up for the M-H 780 combine

780 combine - brake up date and traction modifications

780 combine - Tested on bump track and hill at Moorfield, Kilmarnock.

Baler development

Caldwell cutter - This was a three point mounted pto drive bracken cutter which was never put on the market

Bean concave – for most combine models

Coventry 1960-1963

Potato harvester – modifications – new materials for circular top and also pto testing

Wire grill – MF 35 tractor for warm countries

Trailer - metal all welded

400-500 combines - development

788 combine

Mower - knife development tests at Abbotswood, home of Mr. Harry Ferguson

Baler development - Detail parts made in the workshop included plungers, bale chambers, bale tensioners, bill hooks, sheet metal work.

EX 10 tractor - with 600 cc B.S.A. engine. Not produced, conceived for Africa and prototypes tested in Tanzania.

DX tractors - development. This became the MF 100 series

Tilting tractor cab - not produced. This was the project of Mr Eric Watson and was made at the

Bob Moorcroft seated on the prototype tractor

Maudslay Road workshop, but I never recall seeing it fitted to a tractor.

Reversible plough. This was to become a three furrow reversible.

Seed drill – development including a self-cleaning platform in "punched metal"

Seats development – ergonomics, comfort

Clutches - new friction materials to prevent sticking

Hydraulics - new development on pumps, controls, rams, piping

Welding - introduction of Mig and Tig, new spot welding

Lifting tackle - making appliances to lift and work with in the workshop

Rig Tests - This was a distinct section with premises at Banner Lane and Maudslay Road. Transmissions, gearboxes, wheels, pto units, axles were all tested on "rigs".

As you can imagine, with such a varied output and the fact that some of the projects were never produced or were superseded, every so often room had to be made for new projects. The job of scrapping out sometimes fell to me. On one occasion I can remember when we had by this time moved "Engineering Department" from Fletchamstead Highway to Maudslay Road* in the town centre of Coventry, that room was required. On instructions from on high, "prototype" and master tractors were scrapped by myself – on reflection a tragedy given the way in which the vintage and classic tractor enthusiast movement has now developed – but I was only doing my job! These models included the TE 20, FE 35 and an LTX. They were cut up with acetylene cutters and dumped into a skip. I remember that the TE tractors had red lines painted over all joints with scribing marks across these. In this way any wear or movement could be detected. The LTX was possibly the single prototype that had survived their testing at the Hiatt's farm in Southam (see Derek Hiatt below). Any parts that were not considered useful were also cut up. I really can't recall the exact year but think it was around 1969. The scrapping took place behind the Bailes House.

* *The workshop was temporarily in Banner Lane No. 3 shop between these two.*

Colourful Models, Rounded Designers and that Spanner (USA)

Donald G Bamford

My experiences are a little light. At the time of the merger I was a Senior Layout Draftsman and later an Assistant Project Engineer working principally on utility equipment such as post hole diggers and scraper blades. I started with Harry Ferguson Inc. in November 1946 whilst simultaneously attending night school for a mechanical engineering degree.

At the time of the merger there were two Vice-Presidents of M-H-F. I understand that in high level meetings the two would not recognise each other at the table, and each would address the Chairman as if the other was not there! A battle of wits.

A small thought about that famous Ferguson "fits all" spanner that is commonly talked about. We had a humorous saying about this - "it was only good for a distance throwing competition on a company picnic"!

Al Thornbrough who ultimately became President of M-H-F was a real gentleman in the truest sense of the word. He always had a kind word of support for those he came into contact with.

Mr Klemm who became the ultimate Vice-President of Engineering was a hard taskmaster who used to say "I don't have ulcers – I give them!" He once prepared a group of full size and 12 in. model tractors in a variety of two paint patterns to try to demonstrate the merger of M-H red and the Ferguson grey tractor colours. It eventually became the grey chassis and red sheet metal, but the models also showed grey and yellow, red and dark blue, grey and green etc etc. The problem was to find a distinctive colour scheme that would set M-F apart from the Deere green, Ford grey and blue, Allis Chalmers flambeau red, International Harvester red etc.

My first visit to the UK Engineering group was in 1963 after I had moved to the tractor design section as a Project Engineer. I had approximately annual trips for the next 20 years or so, finally retiring in 1984 as Engineering Manager – Small Tractors.

MF was an excellent place to be an all round engineer. For example, a layout draftsman could design a part or mechanism, he would detail the components, write the shop order to build the parts,

The survivor from the golf course.

That spanner! Two examples of "that" spanner. The top one came with John Farnworth's father's new Ferguson Tractor in 1948, whilst the bottom one is from a North American made tractor in the M-H-F period. There are many variants of these spanners to be collected.

watch the pattern maker make the wood patterns, see the casting being machined, and watch the mechanic assemble and fit the part. It gave everyone full access to the whole process and made for fully rounded designers.

Working Itself Out! (UK and New Zealand)

Keith Base

Keith Base joined Ferguson as an instructor. He was later based in New Zealand where he was personally involved with Sir Edmund Hillary in the training of all his team for the Antarctic Expedition – Keith had set up a small version of the U.K. Stoneleigh training centre there. Here he recalls his feelings about the merger and its aftermath.

Keith has somewhat sad memories of the merger with its apparent disregard of the lesser mortals in the company, the backbiting that went on, and more than anything – a genuine sorrow and despair at the disappearance of a family attitude and devotion to the Ferguson System by many of the Ferguson staff.

"Harry Ferguson himself I am sure became quite dis-illusioned with the end result of the merger of which he had such high hopes," thinks Keith. He believes that an awful lot of people, including the Massey-Harris people, did not appreciate what a unique product they were dealing with and he ventures to suggest from his experience that a lot of people, including dealers, never did understand the Ferguson System. It was not just the tractor but the system of a tractor and whatever implements were used with it. That was the essence of the Ferguson System.

"We at Stoneleigh where I was then already had

Planning the expedition. Edmund Hillary, centre.

knowledge and field experience of the LTX tractor – the Big Fergie." It was super and apparently proved a threat to the established M-H tractors. Keith believes, as do so many others, that it was an act of sheer stupidity on the part of M-H not only to scrap the project but also to scrap the prototypes. Nothing less than industrial vandalism! One reason given for the cancellation of the LTX project was that it couldn't be changed to become a North American style rowcrop style tractor. "What nonsense," says Keith.

Many Ferguson boys left the company or were disposed of in the North American corporate manner! Keith was one of the victims. M-H-F seemed to lose its direction and purpose for the next few years. It seems that Massey-Harris-Ferguson came to be purely a marketing organisa-tion selling all sorts of different tractors.

As Keith says, "That's my view many years on!"

Keith is still a fervent disciple

Hauling in seals to feed the Husky dogs.

of the Ferguson System and until his recent and enduring illness lectured to Farmers' and Young Farmers' Clubs countrywide. He says, "Man always has, apart from a few visionaries like Harry Ferguson, been unable to see the wood for the trees. New ideas, visions and forward thinking people face opposition somewhere – even as did the steam engine!"

He met many people who sold Ferguson tractors largely due to the fact that farmers were simply queuing up to buy them – not because the dealers (apart from a few) ever understood the Ferguson System. This included the M-H dealers right from the start of their involvement. "Sad," laments Keith. However to be fair Keith points out that many M-H field staff with whom he worked did in the end accept that the Ferguson had something to offer and was very different. Ferguson demonstrators ran rings round the M-H equipment in the field – M-H equipment was clumsy and heavy. Some M-H men really did take Ferguson equipment into their hearts! Unfortunately this did not seem to be the case with M-H management! Yet everyone could relate to "It is the Ferguson System that makes the Difference" or "Penetration Without Extra Weight" or "Finger Tip Control" Ferguson slogans.

Keith once recalls doing a sixty mile return trip to see a farmer whose distributor salesman could not use the hydraulic system on the tractor he had sold. Keith had to show him where the lever was which engaged the hydraulic pump!

Keith's final reflection on the merger: "We were certainly sad but it worked itself out after five or six years." Keith is still in touch with many original "Fergie" boys from over 50 years ago and latterly especially through the Ferguson Club in the U.K.

Clearing drift snow to start a Ferguson Tractor.

Unloading supplies at the start of the expedition.

Arrived at the Pole – this tractor pulled the radio cabin.

En route to the South Pole.

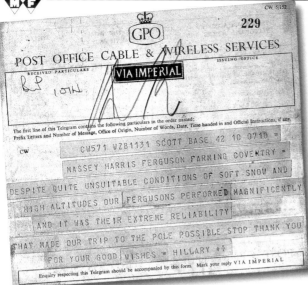

The telegram which was the Ferguson tractors' finest hour.

Commander R. H. Bailey of Massey-Harris-Ferguson Export Division wishing good luck to Dr Vivian Fuchs, Leader of the Transantarctic Expedition, with his Ferguson Tractor.

which has a world-wide membership. "What a wonderful and lasting effect the Grey Fergie and Harry Ferguson himself has left on us."

Preparing for Antarctica

At the time Keith was in New Zealand running a small version of the UK Massey-Harris-Ferguson School of Mechanization at Stoneleigh. Keith had been head of field and workshops there. In New Zealand South Island C B Norwoods had become involved on behalf of M-H-F in working on tractors to be taken to the South Pole. Keith joined in and they tested tractors in the cold and snowy New Zealand Alps. Edmund Hillary was there and they experimented with half tracks. It was Edmund Hillary who suggested and opted for putting tracks over the front and rear wheels. Someone said "you will not be able

to turn, Ed unless you use independent brakes" to which he replied jokingly that he was "not going to turn but go straight to the Pole and beat the Poms!"

Following selection of the tractors that were originally going to be used at Base Camp, Edmund Hillary sent six of his men to Keith's training school at Palmerston North. There he taught them about Fergusons, stripping down and reassembling each machine. The men had lectures and practical experience on engines, gearboxes and hydraulics. Keith says they were super men. He never saw Edmund Hillary again but records how he felt honoured to have taken part in some small way to ensure the success of the team.

TEA 513816, one of the Transantarctic expedition tractors in preservation at the MOTAT Museum, Auckland, New Zealand.

No Animosity (UK)

J R Bibby, Harry Ferguson's Prototype Testers' Foreman

My abiding memory of the amalgamation is the initial feeling of letdown and disillusionment. We thought we were the kings and were going to become ordinary metal benders. From my viewpoint the greatest knock to morale was loss of the big Ferguson LTX tractor. It was superior in performance to anything we knew of and the great hope for the future. I was foreman of the Harry Ferguson prototype testers at the time and had several embarrassments when we bent Massey-Harris small machines but not Harry Ferguson equivalents.

I never sensed any animosity between ourselves and Massey-Harris Manchester or Kilmarnock engineers, personally quite the reverse. The feeling seemed we are stuck together so let's get on with it. I think it was different for the sales people. I remember attending a meeting where an American director said, "we will not listen to criticism of the goods, your job is to sell what you are given. If you don't like it, try down the road." In other words get to work, no more of the implements selling themselves.

Personal Assistant (UK, USA, Canada, USSR, China)

Len Boon

Len Boon always acted as personal assistant to James Duncan whenever he visited the U.K or Europe. After the merger he eventually became Head of the Special Operations Division of Massey Ferguson in 1963 with responsibility for developing manufacturing facilities around the world. The author had the privilege of firstly corresponding with him and then interviewing him in his London club – The Oriental - on March 27th , 2000. He was aged 87 and the author wishes to place on record the amazing grasp of detail which he had of the events of so long ago. The discussions covered his career with Massey-Harris and later Massey Ferguson which started after the war in Toronto in a training unit which was being established. He trained alongside Lionel Massey, son of Vincent Massey. He then worked in most departments and later was sent to work in Kansas, Dallas and the Prairies for six months. Then it was back to the supply department, and finally to the M-H Kansas City Branch.

In 1951 James Duncan (who was born in Paris) started to restructure European Operations after the wartime damages and this is where the working rela-

tionship with Len Boon started to materialise. M-H opened a London Office in Pall Mall and this was key to revamping European operations. Len recalls how in the same period Guy Bevan, Vice-President of M-H Engineering became a close friend of Harry Ferguson – the link that brought Ferguson and Massey-Harris together. Bevan was also in large part responsible for bringing Massey-Harris and Perkins together, with the use of the Perkins P6 engine in Massey-Harris 744 tractors assembled in the U.K. This tractor was primarily conceived for the groundnut scheme in Tanzania – a disaster of a scheme but an ideological shot in the arm for Massey-Harris in the U.K. A few of the 744s were sold in Canada. Len made many trips to Europe with James Duncan reviewing manufacturing programmes.

Finally all events were put in the background due to the Ferguson merger when James Duncan announced that he was flying over the next day. Len plus secretary were ordered to be 100% available and go to the Red Horse Hotel in Stratford immediately. Duncan's wife and son also came over and stayed there – the family acting as camouflage

MASSEY-HARRIS-FERGUSON LIMITED

MANUFACTURERS OF FARM IMPLEMENTS FOR OVER ONE HUNDRED YEARS

HEAD OFFICE TORONTO 3, CANADA

On Board S.S. "Liberté",
November 28th, 1955.

JAMES S. DUNCAN
CHAIRMAN AND PRESIDENT

Personal

Mr. L. J. Boon,
Massey-Harris-Ferguson Ltd.,
35 Davies Street,
London, W.1, England.

Dear Mr. Boon,

I have had a busy time since my arrival on board preparing my Board information and revising my Russian notes, and I do wish to thank you for the most efficient way in which you correlated all the information and for the excellency of the notes taken during our various interviews and business talks.

Mrs. Duncan joins me in thanking you for all you did for us. The efficiency and tact with which you handle all these problems will make it very difficult for those who follow you.

All good luck in the important work which you are now undertaking, but get yourself a good understudy, so that you can travel with us again during my European trip.

Yours sincerely,

Chairman & President.

P.S.   Will you please see that Basil Wedd is reimbursed for the pyjamas, etc., which he bought me upon my return from Russia and charge my personal account.

Len Boon accompanied M-H President James Duncan on his European visits and including this one to Russia.

The humidor showing the mounting of the half crown.

to the events taking place. Len and family joined the group as further camouflage. Len's wife spent time buying "Little Jimmy" Massey-Harris toys of the day!

Len recounted how the Ferguson interest in combines initially brought the two sides together, Ferguson originally viewing Massey-Harris as simply a supplier. Discussions went on for days until it evolved to be a Ferguson sell out! A survey had revealed that Ferguson's side mounted combines were excellent technically and mechanically, but it was deemed that they would not sell because the tractor would be tied up for the duration of the attachment and therefore not available for haulage work etc.

During the merger negotiations James Duncan, on the advice of financial analysts, had become horrified at the exposure Ferguson took and particularly with small companies manufacturing for him. Discussions on the final price ended in the tossing of a coin for one million dollars. Colonel Phillips of Massey-Harris provided the half-crown coin. The toss took place in the back of Ferguson's Rolls Royce where he and Phillips sat together. Ferguson lost the toss. Len was given the task of having the coin framed into a silver cigar box for Harry Ferguson. Shortly after the merger Len accompanied James Duncan and his wife to Paris, travelling on the Golden Arrow on a "Get to Know You" visit to the Ferguson operation there – Duncan regarding France as second only to the U.S.A. in importance of overseas operations.

Len remembers the take-over being painful. He spent days at the Harry Ferguson Fletchamstead Highway office. Alan Botwood, Ferguson's Managing Director, lost his job overnight together with his company car and house. The Ferguson directors had known nothing of the take-over! Harry Ferguson

hired King Edward VII's lawyers to handle the take-over, and they were subsequently hired by Massey-Harris. The Massey-Harris team that moved into Fletchamstead became known as the "Mau-Mau" but the whole take-over procedure was handled with great diplomacy. Harry Ferguson's subsequent and abrupt departure from the tractor scene came as a great surprise to old employees.

James Duncan was approached by the Russians for the Ferguson System and Len accompanied him taking notes for a later James Duncan booklet on the trip. He recalls a huge Russian woman being on security duty outside their massive suite in a Moscow hotel. There was no deal with the Russians but the Chinese later bought 300 Ferguson 35 tractors then copied them and called them "East is Red"!

Len knew Tom Carroll, the famous Massey-Harris combine designer. They didn't always get on! Tom was always making instant design changes to combines already on the combine production line. Len had the job at one time of reviewing the changes and their supply/cost implications. Tom was renown for walking behind combines collecting tailings in his hat to estimate losses. Later a young engineer achieved notoriety when he declared this method to be primitive and in future arranged that 100 yard strips of material should be laid out to collect tailings – progress in evaluation!

The Russians wanted it, the Chinese bought 300 and then copied them calling it "East is Red". This shows the Ferguson 35 being launched at Newsomes, the Ferguson dealership closest to the Banner Lane factory where they were produced.

A Farm by the Factory (Scotland)

John Caldwell

A view from the top of the Caldwell's silage tower showing M-H combines in the background.

Balers in store at the factory about 1950 as viewed from John Caldwell's farm.

John Caldwell farmed land adjacent to the Massey-Harris factory in Kilmarnock, Scotland. He knew many of the people who worked there and his land and crops were often used for machine evaluation and testing. He has two interesting tales of the times:

Shoeing the Horse

One of the employees, Alex Reid, a former blacksmith, worked in the heat treatment section. Alex was in the habit of keeping up his former trade by shoeing horses in his spare time. The owner of a horse, which grazed fields adjacent to the factory asked Alex to shoe his horse. At the time he was on the night shift. He asked his foreman if he could bring the horse into the factory at the tea break to get it shod. The foreman was a person who was always in a rush. When Alex asked the question he had to follow him at a trot up the production line. The foreman did not stop for any discussion but Alex maintained that he answered in the affirmative. At 2 am the horse was in to the welding shop and duly shod, much to the astonishment of management. Alex was able to convince them that he had obtained permission from his foreman and no action was taken against him. This episode was illustrated in the company magazine in cartoon form by a fellow employee, Charlie Ross. The cartoon depicted a painter spraying a line of components. On the line was a horse's head. Alex Reid always maintained that it made him world-famous with the publicity he got in the company magazine.

The Scrap Yard

Bottom: John Caldwell's M-F 780 Combine in stationary mode threshing sheaves.

Near the Kilmarnock factory there was a scrap merchant who dealt with all the scrap metal from the factory. A relative of mine made daily visits to the yard to find what was being scrapped. Over a number of years he was able to collect enough parts to build his own M-H 701 baler! The only part he had to buy from the dealer was a flywheel. The baler operated successfully for many years.

I had the personal experience of being offered a new Perkins P6 engine (as used in M-H 744 tractors) from the scrap yard which was amongst other stuff in a skip. I paid £10 and later sold it to an M-H agent for £30. Later he told me that he installed it in an M-H 780 combine. It only had one fault – it needed a new seal at the drive pulley.

The scrap yard continued its invaluable role into the MF 500 combine era. My 500 gearbox failed and I knew there was a dismantled machine in the scrap yard. Knowing the manager well, I went over the low wall late one evening and took it back to the combine

and fitted it. Next day I went and paid the requested £5. When I asked if he would take the old one as scrap at the same value I was promptly shown the gate! The gearbox lasted the combine's life out on our farm.

A prototype M-H Forage Harvester on trial at John Caldwell's farm next to the Kilmarnock factory.

Production in progress at the Kilmarnock M-H plant. M-H 726 Self-propelled Combines, M-H 744 D Tractors, M-H 701 Balers and M-H 750 Trailed combines

Training at Stoneleigh (UK)

Bob Dickman

F. H. Newsome really was a local Ferguson dealership being the closest to the Banner Lane factory. The site is now a car dealership on the Styvichal roundabout on the A45 road.

I should point out during this period I was only a very junior instructor at Stoneleigh Abbey having joined the Company in December 1955, and as such most of any comments I have would be purely related to training activities on the Ferguson tractor side. Having said this the things I do recall are as follows:

1. I think it's true to say there were enormous cultural differences at that time in the way that Ferguson carried out the training of Dealers/Distributors in both sales and after-sales compared with the Massey-Harris side. The Ferguson side was much more refined and tended to have higher standards of service and repair techniques, e.g. much greater use of special tools, whereas the M-H side relied on more traditional blacksmith type methods - particularly on implements where welding and the use of heavier type repair material was very much the norm. As someone once remarked, it finally took 11 years after the merger before one could say that all M-F Distributors, in terms of their practices and people, were integrated to the point that you were then unable to distinguish between the old Ferguson and Massey-Harris organisations.

2. The Perkins P3 diesel engine conversion for TE Ferguson tractors. Although it created certain problems, we did our best at the time to run specialised conversion courses at Stoneleigh Abbey Training Centre - in particular for those dealers who saw it as a cheaper and more economical conversion than a complete original engine overhaul. There are of course still a few of the P3 conversions running today. I don't think it was the Company's intention at that time to give a great deal of publicity to its availability. However licensee agreements were set up with IMT in Yugoslavia which included the Perkins engine. The P3 engine was therefore an opportunity, and quite popular, for the export side of the business, and no doubt for local assembly and components to be developed.

3. We at the training school, to the best of my recollection, at the time did not run any pre-training courses for the LTX tractor.

4. On the Implement side of the Ferguson training

A Perkins P3 engine fitted into a Ferguson TE type Tractor. Note the raised bonnet. The engine gave the tractor a higher centre of gravity and made it somewhat less stable on sloping land.

An early Ferguson TE Tractor with the first type of 3 ton Ferguson Trailer offered in the UK.

Ploughing at the Ferguson School of Farm Mechanisation.

The Ferguson Transport Box in use at the Training School.

activities we tended to concentrate on the basic implements such as ploughs, tillers, trailers, post hole diggers, transport boxes, loaders, and rear mounted blades, as opposed to the more exotic ones such as mounted combines and a sugar beet harvester. We also worked a range of Industrial Ferguson implements such as road rollers, compressors, and front blades. These were quite popular with the instructors at the weekend for doing various home and garden improvements. Nevertheless we continued to follow

the basic Harry Ferguson philosophy of teaching students the use of the one spanner for all implement adjustments where practical. This certainly proved to be a strong sales and field service argument in favour of the Ferguson implements at that time.

5. The M-H-F 35 tractor. I would say from an instructor point of view that many of us, because we were so conditioned at the time to dealing with the Grey Ferguson design, were quite sceptical when we had to run the first M-H-F 35 "Grey-Gold" tractor

courses. There were areas such as the spur tooth gearbox and cold starting ability on the early models which created a lot of unfavourable remarks at the time - until these were later eventually resolved.

The "grey-gold" Ferguson 35 metamorphosed to become the M-F 35 in M-H-F days. Here a diesel grey-gold and a petrol/tvo MF 35.

Demonstrating a "grey gold" Ferguson 35 Tractor pulling a Ferguson Multi-purpose Seed Drill at the School of Farm Mechanisation

Testing the Ferguson Combine at the Time (USA)

Bob Doll

My initial involvement with Harry Ferguson, Inc. starting in June 1952, was part-time as a student in the College of Engineering at the University of Detroit. The Engineering College offered a Co-operative Education Program. This program was developed with the co-operation of companies who used engineers in their business and could offer students exposure to actual engineering disciplines they could relate to their education. This program added one year of time required to obtain an Engineering Degree since the last two years of course work was stretched into three. For the last three years I continuously alternated between school and work every three months. Upon graduation in June 1955, I joined Massey-Harris-Ferguson as a full time employee.

When I first reported to Harry Ferguson, Inc., as a co-op student, I was assigned to the Design Change Group where approved design changes (requested by manufacturing, suppliers and designers) were processed and changes made to the released drawings. Each work session I was generally assigned to a different part of Engineering to gain varied experience (design, laboratory, field test, etc.) but most of my later work periods were spent in design groups. In those days the design room was a large open room filled with drawing boards. Most of the work at that time involved tractors but some of the engineers were working on ground engaging implements for the

3 point hitch system unique to the weight transfer system used in the Ferguson tractors. Later there was development work on other types of equipment.

Side-Mounted Combine

On my third work session (summer of 1953) I was assigned to the Field Test Department. I was immediately sent to California where test work was underway on a small combine designed by an engineer who was hired after retirement from International Harvester (Melville Mitchell). The combine was side-mounted on a Ferguson TO 30 tractor and powered from the tractor pto. The threshing body was alongside the tractor and the header was offset to cut crop in front of the tractor and combine. Support of the combine was provided on one side by the tractor and on the other side by an outboard wheel which was driven by a shaft attached to the nearest tractor rear wheel. The initial testing was in grain crops using a direct cut header. We changed crops and the location of testing by following the harvest season from south to north in the U.S. Near the end of the summer I was left in charge of the test operation doing test work in Bozeman, Montana. There I received a telegram from the Detroit Office announcing the merger of Harry Ferguson, Inc. with Massey-Harris Ltd. It also stated that the combined companies would be initially known as Massey-Harris-Ferguson. As I recall this name only lasted a short time and was then shortened to Massey-Ferguson.

After the merger, work on the side-mounted combine stopped since Massey-Harris was well established in combine

A tanker version of the Ferguson Side-mounted Combine being tested in North America. It had a different and simpler mounting to the tractor than British made models. Here it is seen with optional quick attach engine

Above: This machine is thought to be an American version of the Ferguson Side-mounted Combine.

Right: Single and two-row corn pickers were eventually marketed for the M-F65, 85 and Super 90 Tractors. These two examples were shown in M-F's 1963 catalogue. But in fact there was nothing new about this concept – M-H had offered the same type of equipment in the past!

harvesters. From Massey's point of view they wanted the relationship with Ferguson to enhance their position in the tractor market. The Massey tractors of that era were quite out of date and certainly did not have a Ferguson style three point hitch and weight transfer system.

Corn Pickers and Hay Wafering

When I started my full time employment with Massey-Harris-Ferguson Engineering in June of 1955, I was assigned to the Implement Design Section to work on developing a mounted One Row Cornpicker for the smaller Ferguson Tractors. The design responsibility was divided among two engineers, one for the Snapping Unit and the other for the Husking Bed. I was assigned the Snapping Unit. We designed, built and tested several prototypes but the design was never released for production. At the end of this program,

28

MASSEY-FERGUSON MF 48 HAY PACKER
A COMPLETELY NEW CONCEPT IN HAY MAKING

The M-F 48 Hay Packer with which Bob was involved. It did not achieve wide success despite having the potential to considerably reduce hay transport costs by producing a denser product than hay bales.

in late 1956, I was transferred to the Engineering Research Group. This was a small group, headed by Dr. Mark, where several new concept projects were being investigated. Among those projects were Hydrostatic Transmissions for tractors and Hay Wafering & Pelletizing. Most of my time in this group was spent on Hydrostatic Transmission development. We designed, prototyped and tested several transmissions which were tested in the laboratory and installed in an MF-35 tractor. There were many problems encountered in our efforts to develop a functionally satisfactory, reliable unit which would meet the cost objectives. Eventually the project was dropped, primarily because the Research Group was eliminated.

In late 1958, I was transferred to the Tractor Design Group where work was underway to develop larger Farm Tractors (the MF 85, 88 and 90 Models). The rest of my design experience with MF involved tractors. In 1975 I moved into Engineering Management where more of my time was spent dealing with plans, schedules, budgets, personnel and communication with other departments.

The M-F 85 was the first of M-F's higher horsepower tractors released in 1959.
It incorporated the Ferguson System. This is a rowcrop model.

The M-F Super 90 Tractor was the biggest of the first group of higher horsepower post-merger tractors. It was available with diesel or petrol engine and used the Ferguson System hydraulics. The MF 85, 88 and 90 Tractors preceded MF's next series of tractors – the MF 100s and 1000s launched in 1964-1965. It therefore took almost 10 years from the merger to produce a new comprehensive line of tractors.

An Iowa Ferguson and Massey Dealer (USA)

Ted Feekes

Ted became a Ferguson dealer in 1950. By 1952, he was losing business to International Harvester (Farmall's) because the farmers were looking for larger, row crop tractors. That year he took on the Massey-Harris line to give him larger, row crop tractors and combines to sell. He retained his Ferguson dealership. Ted's Shop may have been somewhat unique in having both the Ferguson and Massey-Harris franchises before the merger. The quality of the Ferguson tractors was very clear when compared to the Massey-Harris products. Ted's Shop sold Massey-Harris 33s, 44s, 333s and 444s as well as Ferguson TO-20s, 30s and 35s during this period.

The merger was a time of uncertainty for the dealer. They didn't know who the next distributor would be and who would be the salesman for M-H-F. Ted's Shop continued to get tractors from both Massey and Ferguson after the merger.

Due to the uncertainty at the time it was difficult to know what to promote. A new large Ferguson tractor was talked about as well as a Ferguson combine.

Looking back, these were two big companies with agricultural equipment trying to integrate distributors, salesman and dealers. As a dealer, you wondered where this was heading.

The merger took some of the fun out of promotion. Promotions weren't as good as in the Ferguson days. An example of a fun and effective promotion in the Ferguson days was a "Field night" that was set up by the Ferguson salesman. Using floodlights at night it was a good way to draw farmers to demonstrations. One demonstration had the Ferguson rake moving balloons without popping them. This promotional creativity was just not present after the M-H-F merger.

The Ferguson Side-delivery Rake was used at night-time demonstrations to move balloons about without bursting them – sure evidence of the gentle handling of hay by the machine.

Cutter bar cuts at wide range of angles: up to 90° above horizontal (under full hydraulic control), and up to 45° below horizontal. Available in 5, 6 or 7 foot lengths.

DYNA-BALANCE DRIVE eliminates vibration.

Double-throw crank shaft is accurately counter-balanced to eliminate vibration, permitting sustained high mowing speeds. Drive forces are in same plane as the knife. All rotating and oscillating joints have sealed anti-friction bearings.

FERGUSON *Dyna-Balance* INDUSTRIAL MOWER FEATURES

As well as farm use the Ferguson Dyna-balance Mower was used extensively for industrial and amenity use because it could angle 90° above horizontal and 45° below.

After the merger, there appeared to be more quality problems. Examples:

1. Two forage wagons came in from Massey with poor paint and minus parts that had been "robbed" off of them. Replacement parts came in from two different distributors, one from as far off as New York. This added to the confusion and involved excess freight costs.

2. In one shipment he received 6 dyna-balance mowers – but three without bars! M-H-F insisted that Ted's Shop pay in full even though parts were missing.

3. Quality on the M-H-F tractors seemed to be good through the 1950s. In the 1960s with the introduction of the 165-175-180 series, many quality problems showed up in clutches, transmission and power steering. The dealership did not get good support from distributors on warranty parts.

In the 1960s M-F seemed to try to have more control over the dealer. Ted's Shop sold other lines of implements including Kewanee Discs and Mulchers. The M-F salesman was on a quota and threatened to cancel Ted's franchise if he didn't stop selling these other lines to concentrate fully on M-F!

Another Stoneleigh Instructor's Memories of the M-H-F Period (UK)

Colin Fraser

I became an instructor at Stoneleigh in 1956 almost by accident. M-H-F had launched a recruitment drive for people they thought could become future high-flyers in the company called the New Entry Trainee scheme. I applied and was called to Stoneleigh Abbey for an interview. It was one of those intimidating panel interviews with three elderly gentlemen sitting behind a table while I sat in front of them. One of them was the famous Captain Duncan Hill, the head of the Stoneleigh Training Centre. He was once heard describing himself on the phone as being "big, bald, and bloody rude", but on this occasion he and the other interviewers were rather avuncular and the experience was not too harassing, even for a callow 21-year-old like me.

A few days later I received a letter saying that I had not been accepted for the New Entry Trainee scheme but that Captain Hill would like me to be a trainee instructor at Stoneleigh. It actually made no difference because all of the New Entry Trainees also became trainee instructors at Stoneleigh as the first step in their supposedly meteoric career. However, most of them were old Etonians and Oxbridge graduates while I had been to an agricultural college and worked on farms. Perhaps the fact that I spoke fluent French and German made Duncan Hill think I might be useful in his training centre. In fact, in the subsequent years, it was Erik Fredriksen - who also speaks French and whose memories appear here - and I who gave all of the Stoneleigh courses that were in French.

On arriving at Stoneleigh I was assigned to the Field Section. This was the Section that gave courses in the use of the Ferguson System and its implements. The instructors in the Section were all old Harry Ferguson hands and imbued with his crusading spirit. It was highly infectious and I soon fell under its spell. Most convincing of all was Keith Base, an ex-wartime pilot who had been badly burned in his crashing Spitfire. He was my guide and mentor as I went through the process of becoming a qualified instructor, learning about the technical aspects of the equipment and how to teach about it. But Keith also inculcated in me the Ferguson philosophy of farm mechanization.

It was this that certainly led later to my writing the biography of Harry Ferguson, first published in 1972 and re-published in a paperback edition* in 1998.

Harry Ferguson. Inventor and Pioneer by Colin Fraser

Despite the enormously satisfying work of being an instructor on the "grey" range of tractors and equipment, the M-H-F days were in general not too happy. The Stoneleigh team was a bunch of very congenial and amusing people, but there was quite a lot of sniping between the "red" and the "grey" factions. There was an oft repeated moan from the grey faction. "The Old Man has sold us down the river." (The "Old Man" was of course Harry Ferguson).

Troubles with the grey and gold FE 35 tractor did not help morale. The four-cylinder engine with its rotary injection pump and its Ricardo Comet cylinder head was the very devil to start on cold mornings. And none of the "greys" liked the adoption of twin levers to control the hydraulic system. I was once sent off on a lecture tour in northern England and Scotland to explain how the hydraulic system worked and how to use the levers correctly. Groups of up to 200 farmers turned up to these evening lectures. At one of them, in Hexham, I finished my lecture and asked the farmers if they had any questions. A bluff Yorkshire man stood up and said loudly, "Everything you've told us is all well and good and it's very clear, but it's completely useless if the bloody tractor won't start in the morning!" He had a very good point, but by the greatest strokes of fortune, there was a technical man from the then Lucas CAV company on the tour with me. So I was able to throw the hot potato to him.

There seemed to be a general feeling, at least at Stoneleigh, that the old Ferguson emphasis on quality was being subverted by the M-H influence. An increasing interest in making profits rather than on making excellent machinery seemed to be at work. The "red" faction maintained that HF was suffering large losses before the merger and that that was the reason for Harry Ferguson making his deal with M-H. Be that as it may, there were incidents that proved the "greys" were right about the quality issue. For example, one day a fellow instructor was ploughing in the Stoneleigh Deer Park with a new M-H-F plough. He caught a large tree root and returned with a bent plough beam.

The "grey" faction was scandalized. "That would never, ever, have happened with the old HF ploughs" they said. "The Old Man promised a fiver to anyone who bent a plough beam in normal work, and nobody ever did." They were referring to the massive forged steel beams manufactured by Rubery Owen and used on the original Harry Ferguson ploughs.

Others have doubted the wisdom of introducing the two-lever control for the hydraulic system on the FE 35 especially for developing countries. I saw the problem for myself when I spent three months in Madagascar for M-H-F. My task was to visit as many of the 130 or so Ferguson tractors in the island and talk with their owners and operators, in effect to wave the company flag and show the tractor owners that they were "not forgotten in their lost corner of the world", as the distributor put it.

With a member of the distributor's staff, I travelled all over the enormous island in a 2 CV. We went to one village that had very recently taken delivery of an FE 35. We found that the three-furrow plough had been partly dismantled leaving it as a single furrow one. I asked the villagers why they had taken off two of the bodies. They told me that the tractor would not pull all three. The tractor and plough were the biggest investment they had ever made and they were very disappointed.

I told them we were going to rebuild the plough immediately and I would show them that the tractor would plough three furrows comfortably. They clearly did not believe me and said I should try the tractor with the single furrow first. But I politely refused and we started to rebuild the plough. By the time it was ready the whole village was in attendance and we made our way to a nearby field. I asked the tractor driver to try the plough first, but he made very little progress because he was using the position control lever only. The crowd of villagers remained silent, probably thinking me a complete idiot - and an arrogant one too for not believing them.

I asked the driver to get off, settled into his seat myself and within seconds was pulling

three furrows 9 inches deep in the red soil. I spent the next half hour or more giving one-on-one tuition to the driver on the use of position control, draft control, and response control until he too had the tractor purring across the field turning three good furrows. The villagers were delighted, and as we left they rushed to our 2 CV bringing gifts of live chickens, eggs, and fruit, hardly the most practical of gifts for our itinerant existence but a wonderful gesture of gratitude towards us for getting them out of their muddle with the two levers - which probably should not have been there in the first place.

In my last years at Stoneleigh, we instructors came under increasing pressure to make our training courses more sales oriented. Management said that Stoneleigh was costing the company a great deal of money and they wanted to see a more direct return on it This ran counter to the HF philosophy, which was that excellent farm machinery and people well trained in its correct use and maintenance was the best way to promote sales. And under this philosophy, instructors were expected never to denigrate equipment made by competitors. The "grey" faction at Stoneleigh did not take too kindly to the changing ethic. Many of them left, myself included.

Ferguson
8" THREE FURROW PLOUGH
Mainly for shallow and stony soils this latest addition to the Ferguson range has lea type bodies which, with their gently curved mouldboards, leave an unbroken and well set up furrow slice, suitable, if necessary, for broadcasting the subsequent crop.

Colin Fraser refers to the three furrow Ploughs. They were usually 10 in. furrows but some were made as 8 in. versions – now quite rare to find.

Ferguson 10" THREE FURROW PLOUGH

Designed for faster ploughing of medium and light soils, this plough can be supplied as a conversion set for the 10" two furrow plough. As with all Ferguson Ploughs, it is made of high grade steels and materials, and is of rugged construction capable of standing up to the hardest wear.

Confessions of a "Grey Man" (who became a red and grey!)
(UK, Denmark)

Erik Fredriksen

Erik had the good fortune to drive a Ferguson Brown as far back as 1947. Here enthusiast David Bull puts a restored Ferguson Brown through its paces.

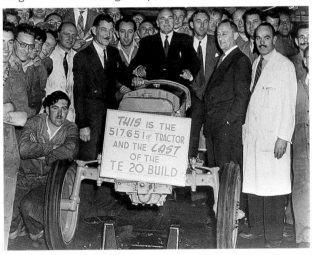

Erik loved the grey TE style grey Fergusons. The last coming off the line would have been a sad moment for him.

I joined Massey-Harris-Ferguson on 13th February, 1956 as an instructor in the M-H-F School of Mechanisation at Stoneleigh. My mechanisation upbringing to that stage was definitely Ferguson "grey". I drove my first tractor, a Ferguson Brown on steel wheels in the summer of 1947 in Norway during my farming upbringing period before coming to England in 1952 after finishing agricultural college

where I graduated as an agronomist.

After 1947 it was back to horses for a while, but the farmer I was working for at the time saw the light and bought a TE 20. Not much good to me as I could not get him off the seat to let me have a go! I had to sneak into the shed to get the feel for it, very frustrating.

After college the students were offered a one year "Student Exchange" scheme with England or France. I chose England as in my view at the time it was the most mechanised and that was what I was interested in. I was lucky as my first farm was Timewells Farm, Washingborough, near Lincoln with Mr and Mrs Large. They were nice people, and they owned a TE 20 which had recently been delivered from Wests of Lincoln, the local dealer. Well, I had the same problem as with my Norwegian TE 20 farmer, I could not get him off the seat and was relegated to drive the Fordson N. After a while Mrs Large, who held quite a sway in the household, agreed that as a student I should learn the "Ferguson System" and so I got to drive the TE 20 on a more regular basis. I had a wonderful time in Lincolnshire.

My second farm was with a friend of the Large family in Kent/Sussex, a Mr Jack Merrick, a progressive fruit farmer who was in a big apple growing area near Wincheslea in Sussex. I actually finished up on one of his farms in Kent. They had plenty of tractors, a new Fordson Major, a new Major track conversion and some TE 20s. I was given a TE 20 of my own - would you believe it? My own tractor, that I was totally responsible for! I drove every day; a range of implements, and life was interesting. I even sneaked in some fun driving Fords as well. Yes, they were big and powerful, but by then I appreciated the nimbleness of the TE 20, and at the end of the day it competed well on work done, and for someone interested in mechanisation that was important.

I returned to Norway after my year's apprenticeship in the U.K. which turned out to be a conversion to the "Ferguson System" way of farming. After a winter of working in the forest of a large holding in Norway I got itchy feet and consulted the job pages of the Farmers Weekly, where I found a vacancy at Lawnswood Farm, Wordsley near Stourbridge in

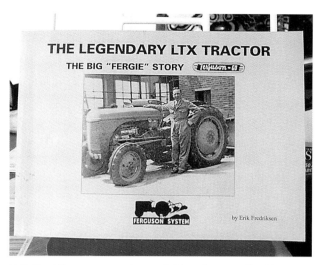

Erik Fredriksen prepared a useful brochure on the Ferguson LTX Tractor which is still available.

Worcestershire. Tractor driver on a Ferguson System farm; interesting work with the latest mechanisation equipment. Well I could not resist that so off went the application and I got the job.

The farm as it turned out was owned by Mr Jack Bean, who owned factories in Wolverhampton and Tipton. This Mr Bean is the same person mentioned in the merger talks between Massey-Harris and Ferguson, as he was a supplier to both companies, and acquainted with the management of both. He supplied implements on contract to Harry Ferguson, and castings for the MH 745 tractor and other components for Massey-Harris. Anyway as a result of his contacts he must have obtained equipment at the "right price" for the farmyard was literally covered with Ferguson implements plus an M-H combine and baler. Again I was given my own tractor and used a wide range of implements regularly through the season. Wonderful!

In addition to this, one of Jack Bean's factories, Midland Industries, made what I think was the best loader in the world at the time. The MIL loader was unbeatable, and I became a demonstrator and test driver of the loader; I travelled in the UK and Europe and beat everything in sight. The TE 20 and MIL loader was an awesome combination for shifting muck or dirt. Midland Industries had a stand at the British Pavilion in 1955 inside the Tivoli Gardens in Copenhagen. All our own loaders were on display and demonstrated. Among the visitors came the Ferguson tractor importers from all over Scandinavia, and I met them all - very good contacts for the future.

They told me about the wonderful acceptance of the Ferguson System and the resulting tractor sales. I had become very hooked on the "little grey" by then, so much so that I asked Jack Bean if he could get me a job in the Ferguson organisation.

By that time the fact that the company had been taken over by Massey-Harris had not had much impact on me. I was only interested in the "Ferguson System". The "red" side was of no concern to me. But that was to change.........

With Jack's contacts I successfully applied for a job as instructor at the M-H-F School of Farm Mechanisation at Stoneleigh. That is when the "red and grey" impact of the merger struck me for the first time. As a TE 20 tractor driver "out there" on the farms I had heard little about it, and it did not seem to affect me personally. The dealer politics were unknown to me. Farmers who bought the products were no doubt more affected.

By 1956 the training for the integrated staff of both M-H and Ferguson dealerships was in full swing. The "grey" had to learn about the M-H 780 combine and 701 baler and the "red" men had to learn about the "Ferguson System" and TE 20 tractors. This worked well at Stoneleigh mainly because the instructors were "nice guys" keen to learn about the other side as well as imparting their knowledge to students coming in. We must not forget that both products were very popular and well accepted on farms. The "reds" accepted that the Ferguson System worked well and was successful. The "greys" also accepted that the M-H 780 combine was an excellent product selling well, the 701 baler probably was not seen as such a success. The one product the "greys" could not accept was the M-H tractor line. Totally outdated and a natural enemy of what the Ferguson System stood for: they were heavy, cumbersome and dangerous, with little or no sophistication. They belonged to the depths of Africa on big cotton or sugar plantations, where brute force and toolbar rowcrop work were the order of the day, and of course Stoneleigh's "red" staff conducted a tropical agriculture course where the virtues of the M-H 745 tractor were explained. In no way did these tractors belong in the Ferguson mechanisation progress.

Keith Base was my instructor in the introductory period at Stoneleigh. An inspiring person he was. The Ferguson System was his life and part of his soul ...... dear Keith. Ian McKenzie, another good instructor, also helped my total conversion to the grey

A Ghana Goodwill and Trade Mission visits M-H-F in Coventry. M-H-F instructor Mr G Lloyd-Jones rides with Mr W Baidoe Ansah as he tries out an M-F 35 Tractor (note an early model still with the Ferguson badge) at the M-F School of Farm Mechanisation at Stoneleigh.

Below left: Erik condemned the M-H tractor range as " belonging to the depths of Africa". This 1952 advertisement shows the pre-merger range which really changed very little to the end of the M-H-F period.

camp and dedication to the Ferguson ideals.

The "greys" saw themselves as engineers whereas they considered the "reds" as "blacksmiths and tin bashers" with accuracy to within a quarter of an inch! The "reds" considered the "greys" to be arrogant and know-alls. This is probably a bit extreme but the underlying feeling was there. As I said the atmosphere between instructors was very good by the time I joined; we were all friends doing a good job. Many "grey" people however felt betrayed by Harry Ferguson. How could he sell out to a bunch of blacksmiths?

The problems, uncertainties and bitterness were also out in the dealerships. Who was to be "red" or "grey"; who was getting what? On this I was not involved and cannot comment. One point I can comment on from my research* on LTX tractors is that the few top people and grass roots staff on the development work for this tractor were very bitter about the decision of M-H-F not to go ahead with this outstanding tractor. This was seen as a betrayal, not just to us "greys" who worked on the project but to have been by Harry Ferguson himself.

* see Erik's booklet: The Legendary LTX Tractor. The Big "Fergie" Story.

It took a long time to settle down as a happy family. We must not forget that this was the first merger of two agricultural empires, both with proud traditions: M-H an historical one and Harry Ferguson a techno-logical one.

Above right: The "reds" accepted that the Ferguson System worked well; the "greys" that the M-H 780 Combine was an excellent product. And so M-H and Ferguson came together to use the best of their product lines. This is the front of an early M-F tractor and equipment brochure.

I called this article "Confessions of a Grey Man" for good reasons. In 1956 I became part of a team who felt very loyal to Harry Ferguson ideals. We had a mission .... simple as that!

Today mergers go on and off all the time; it is an accepted way of life, but I am sure it does not create a happy, contented life for the people involved at the time, no more than it did in the early fifties when M-H and Ferguson decided to join forces. Although we did eventually "merge" and have a contented life. I did anyway!

The Birth of Stoneleigh Training School, then Onwards for 42 years (UK)

John Garlick

I started with Fergusons in 1957. By this time the Massey-Harris takeover was done.

My first job was at Stoneleigh Deer Park. This was built as an American army hospital in the war and comprised over one hundred buildings, all of which were derelict. At that time, just the opposite to the present day, the government was keen to reclaim all land for food production under their scheme Land Reclamation.

In this first job I worked for Griff Jones the farm manager. The main machines used for reclaiming the land were Ferguson TEF tractors, Ferguson subsoilers and Ferguson single furrow 16" ploughs; for grubbing out trees and bush we used a Massey-Harris 745 tractor fitted with a Broughton winch. I remember on one occasion we had the front wheels high in the air - the axle pin fell out and the front axle fell off!

The Deer Park site was leased by Massey-Harris-Ferguson from Lord Leigh of Stoneleigh Abbey. At that time the Ferguson Training Centre was housed at Stoneleigh Abbey horse stables. With the increase of the M-H-F product range it quickly became too small, hence the take-over of the Deer Park camp and land.

A great deal of time and money was spent on the 200 acre Deer Park site to convert the hospital buildings into workshops and lecture rooms. The Training Manger was the Captain Duncan Hill. With his naval background he demanded the best from everyone and he surrounded himself with ex-military men who lived in fear of his voice. The result was the largest and best kept training centre in the world!

In the U.K. a heavy duty Series 2 Broughton Winch could be fitted to the last series of British built M-H Tractors – the M-H 745. It weighed 11 cwt. and would pull 10 tons.

The site of the M-F School of Farm Mechanisation which utilised a wartime American Air Force hospital.

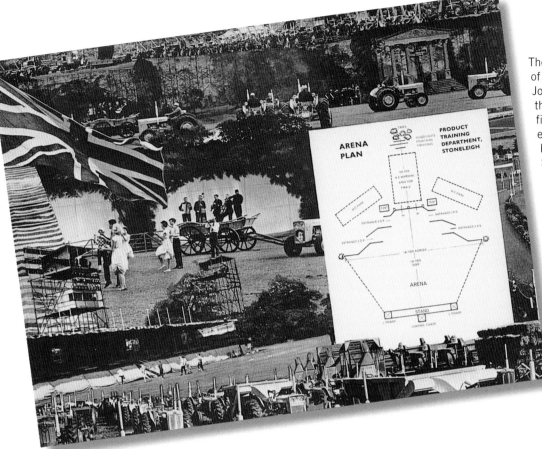

The 1961 M-F Pageant of the Pacesetters. John believed that this was one of the finest spectacles ever staged by M-F. It was held at the Stoneleigh based Product Training Department. This is a collage of various sights from the show taken from the brochure produced for the event.

M-F made both an In-Line and Offset flail type Forage Harvester and both had 40 in. cuts.

I recall when we demolished some twenty buildings with TE 20 tractors fitted with high lift ("banana") loaders that we burnt out nine clutches converting the site into a cricket pitch that the Captain could see from his office, and of course all of the remaining buildings were painted in battleship grey.

Just a note on the "Pageant of the Pacesetters". I took part in this fantastic show. One person who should take special credit for the musical ride of tractors was Ted Staines, then the tractor training supervisor. However when Captain Hill was having a bad day he would refer to it as the "Pageant of the P..s Potters"!!

I recall the introduction of the MF 711 Potato Harvester. The prototype was built at Silsoe out of scrap metal. At that time it was the only harvester that could harvest tulip bulbs without damaging them. If you spent a few hours on that machine watching the turntable go round, then look at the sky, the sky would also revolve!

From the farm I went to work in the School parts and stores for some time before training to become an instructor on the harvesting machines. The machines I worked on were the finger bar mowers, rotary mowers, forage harvesters; 15/20, 703, 124, 126 and round balers; 187, 487, 500, 510, 525, 625, 92 combine harvesters – all Scottish, French, Danish or North American products. The dealer combine course would run for two weeks. In that time a machine would be completely stripped down and re-built to

factory specification.

From the School I joined the Service department on exports. I travelled the world for some years training and trouble-shooting machines. Then I joined the UK Service Department and retired in 1999.

John worked with many combines from the old style M-H 92 to later types such as the M-F 525.

The demonstration hall of the School of Farm Mechanisation at Stoneleigh in M-H-F days. Note the mix of M-H, Ferguson and M-F equipment and tractors.

Field Testing the "Innovative" Baler and Forage Harvester (USA)

D.E. "Del" Gentner

"Del" Gentner teaching about injection systems on diesels at the M-F Training Centre in Indianapolis in 1963.

"Del" Gentner at his Warranty Specification desk at M-F, Des Moines in 1986.

Field Testing

My first look at the baler was at the Ferguson Product Farm at Ann Arbor Trail in Ann Arbor, Michigan. The demonstrator was Ed Malevich, the man who had demonstrated Harry Ferguson's Ferguson Brown tractor to Henry Ford at Dearborn. Ed showed a group of Ferguson service and marketing personnel the proper way to approach the demonstration of this newly designed piece of hay toolage. We assembled and set up this new unit from scratch. Then Ed showed us the proper way to hook the unit to the tractor, using both the outboard wheel drive and the pto hook up, and how to make all necessary adjustments to the unit.

Following this phase of the demonstration we went out into the alfalfa field where everyone had an opportunity to drive the tractor-baler and to bale both flat and hilly terrain. This included the use of the outboard drive and all types of operations. Over a four day period Malevich prepared us how to properly demo the unit in all conditions.

Next we were given a similar, intensive training programme with the F-HO-20 forage harvester.

We then had a demonstration for dealers at Birch

Leon Parker demonstrating the Side-mounted Baler in Michigan.

Two of the most innovative and advanced implements were the semi-mounted B-E-20 "Tractor Mate" Baler and the F-HO-20 "Tractor Mate" Forage Harvester. The history of the two machines was interesting, short and shrouded in corporate mystery.

At the time I was serving as the Service Manager for Farm Supply Inc., the Ferguson Distributor for Michigan. Some of my reflections are quite personal, but they did happen. Some of the photos shown here were ones I took and some were in the engineering shop. These units were all prototypes and were in the process of field and engineering testing. Some of these prototype units were being shown to marketing and dealer personnel.

Three photos of the Ferguson Side-mounted Forage Harvester in action.

Run, Michigan. We used a TO-35 tractor with the forage harvester, showing dealer personnel and Ferguson personnel the operational units in actual field operations. At each demo there were from 20-30 people present.

There was great dealer interest in some areas, but not in all. This was primarily due to the fact that units had to be used on Ferguson or Ford tractors. But both units were well accepted by most Ferguson dealers and there were numerous baler and forage harvester demonstrations throughout the USA. A number of these revolutionary designed units were sold but the overwhelming number of balers and forage harvesters being sold throughout the country were pull types.

Farmers' Week

A second showing of the baler and forage harvester took place at the Farmers' Week in Michigan at the end of January 1955. We had an inside display as well as an outdoor demonstration to show the ease with which the unit could be hooked up to the tractor, even in cold, snowy and slippery conditions! District Service Managers Charles Wells, Clyde Perkins and myself took turns outside and had quite a lot of fun doing it. The new type of side mounted equipment drew a great deal of attention and some sales commitments were made. A number of Michigan Ferguson dealers manned the display. We also showed the Ferguson TO-35 tractor and the D-EO rake. Another display was a cutaway of the Ferguson Hydraulic system and we took turns demonstrating its operation. It was a good week for all of us involved.

In the spring of 1956 M-H-F introduced the Ferguson F-40 tractor, several months after the former M-H dealers had been given the new M-H 50 tractor. Both of these tractors provided opportunity for even greater use of the baler and forage harvester,

Solving the Knotter Riddle

We discovered that we were having some problems with the knotter, particularly with certain brands of twine. I was requested to check with Charlie Powers, a Service Field Engineer for the Ferguson Division of M-H-F. I lived about 40 miles from the Powers Farm, so I drove down there each day for several days to work on the knotter problem.

We found the thickness variation of some twine was too great for the knotter to properly tie the knots. After adjusting and readjusting the knotter and not solving the problem, we determined that the International Harvester knotter was the culprit. I jokingly suggested that we should try the knotter from the Ferguson F 12 baler! It was similar to the knotter that had been used successfully on the M-H No. 3 baler. There was a prototype F 12 baler in the shed. We worked all night and for the next couple of days on the changeover. We were beat, but we headed for the field. We adjusted the knotter several times with the same twine and baler we had been using. We decided to go to work and we didn't miss a knot in 105 bales!

I then went home and got a good night's sleep, returning the next morning. Under normal conditions, the hay was too moist to bale, but I found Charlie out there in the field doing a beautiful job of baling. After a couple of cups of coffee we went back to the field and baled all day. We ran out of hay but found a neighbour who had some heavier hay. We made some minor adjustments and baled for the balance of the day with only five defective bales.

The next task was Charlie's: to tell and sell the Engineering Department on the "unauthorised engineering change" and the profit of the B-E-O balers' perfect operation after the change. It was handled with no known problem. Charlie had done a good job of selling the changeover. Before long, the change was made and the Johnson Knotter had found its home on the B-E-O baler.

This was really my first experience in the operation, servicing and selling the side mounted baler. It was an excellent piece of equipment and a number were sold. I was aware of only what had been sold in Michigan. At the time of recall of the baler, there had been 27 of them sold. Of the forage harvester, there were 11 sold I believe.

Demonstrating the Side-mounted Baler.

The Recall and Destruction

In 1957 M-H-F recalled all the balers and forage harvesters. No records can be found of the total number of units either recalled or produced. The company offered to exchange each unit that had been sold with a conventional baler or forage harvester of the customer or dealer's choice. The branch service personnel were directed to cut up and destroy all units. The orders came from M-H-F management, Ferguson Division Engineering, and the Service Department.

No excuses were given nor were any explanations offered. It is my idea that we were too far ahead of the times. If it were today or even in the '70s with all the three point systems and the independent/live PTO systems, we could have made it work. We possibly could have demonstrated the B-E-O baler and the F-H-O forage harvester on our competitors' as well as on our own tractors and set a new trend.

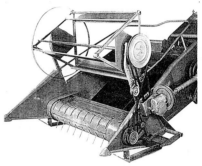

Above: Design of the pick up table of the Ferguson Side-mounted Forage Harvester

Left: A Ferguson Side-mounted Forage Harvester mounted on a Ferguson TO-30 Tractor.

Above: Design of the cutting table of the Ferguson Side-mounted Forage Harvester

Left: Ferguson Side-mounted Baler with auxiliary Ferguson engine fitted. Note the three point hitch facility for the engine.

Above: A Side-mounted Baler in action in Wisconsin, USA. Inset: The Ferguson Side-mounted Baler detached from the tractor.

Today, a handful of both machines still exist. For whatever reasons, a few owners refused to turn their machines over to M-H-F and accept an exchange. They are now considered rare and are much sought after by collectors.

Once more, Ferguson was too far ahead of the times.

(This contribution by Del Gentner was originally prepared for "Ferguson Furrows" Issue No. 7 August 2002. Del and the editor are thanked for their kind permission for it to be reproduced here)

A TO 35 tractor, Side-mounted Baler and Forage Harvester at the Michigan State University where the equipment was demonstrated.

"The Circus Comes to Town" (UK)

Recollections of the MF Demonstration Department in the Late 50s and Early 60s

Bob Gilchrist

Live working demonstrations were everything to Harry Ferguson. Here he (left) is observing one of his early hand lift plough designs fitted to a Fordson Tractor.

Harry Ferguson (left) watches performance in 1921 of hand lift plough with embryonic Ferguson system.

I joined the MF Demonstration Department based at Fletchamstead Highway, Coventry in 1959. Peter Delingpole was the Demonstration Manager. He was the hard-working, hard-playing extrovert type demanding very high standards at the same time living life to the full. A wonderful and thoroughly professional boss to have, who carried forward the legendary Harry Ferguson standards and traditions.

The tractors and implements were maintained to the highest standards both visually and performance wise. Staff were turned out in immaculate white overalls with red cuffs and grey collars, MF neck ties and white shirts, almost military fashion right down to the minute detail. Let me try to illustrate some of these points.

We had a dedicated fleet of MF 35 and 65 tractors with a range of ploughs and soil engaging implements (see p106). When a new tractor was added to the fleet it was first of all sent to Engineering Department to have 200-300 hours run up on a dynamometer to bed the engine and to ensure it was exactly within the advertised performance figures – no higher and no lower.

On completion of that it was taken to the demonstration workshops at the Stoneleigh Training Centre where it was prepared for action. This included removing all three point linkage and removing paint from all the ball joints, making them free to rotate with the finger tips, loader tipping pipes, automatic hitches, stabiliser brackets, inner front wheel weights, rear wheel water ballast were all fitted. 35 tractors were often specified with PAVT rear wheels, the object being to make the tractors as easy as possible to set up for whatever demonstration should come along.

We had a number of slave tractors, one was a grey

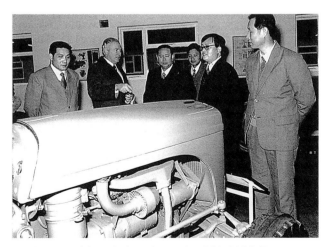

Far Eastern visitors being shown the 500,000th Ferguson TE tractor by Bob at the M-F Training Centre.

and gold 35 complete with rear mounted spray kit used to keep the fleet looking like new at every demonstration. Another was a 35 complete with loader for loading and off loading ploughs and cultivators at demo sites and erecting flagpoles. A number of 723 post hole diggers were also part of the back up equipment.

It should be remembered that although at demonstrations the equipment looked as though it had just come straight off the production line it was all very much hard-working kit. As demonstrators we spent hours in all weathers washing, cleaning and polishing. All implements had their three point linkage pins polished to facilitate easy hitch up. We spent time practising backing up to implements so that the three points could be attached without movement of either the tractor or the implement, each ball end must slide on the pin perfectly. All the ploughs would be used in the field until the mouldboards were totally smooth and polished and then sprayed with anti-rust fluid. Indeed any machine in the fleet had to have been used and set up before it ever was considered for a demonstration. I can assure you the best way to learn about any piece of equipment is to wash, clean and polish it, you soon get to know where every nut and bolt is!

Most UK distributors and dealers had their own demonstrator, often a salesman or sometimes the delivery lorry driver. These were very competent and knowledgeable about local conditions and require-

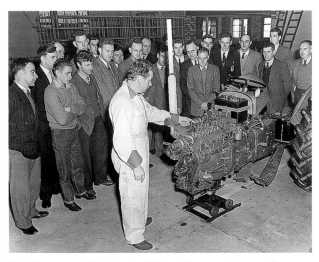

Training was at the heart of Harry Ferguson's operations and he developed one of the world's finest tractor and implement training (demonstrations and servicing) organisations around the world with the heart of operations at the Stoneleigh School of Farm Mechanisation. Here an instructor teaches the features of Ferguson 35 Tractor.

ments and expert at "on the farm" demonstrations. This meant the MF demonstration team was called on for Distribution Open Days, local shows, The Royal Show (which in those days moved around the UK each year), The Royal Highland, Royal Welsh, ploughing matches, forestry exhibitions, launches, promotions, etc, etc.

Part of Bob's activities included service training for the Bord Na Mona (Irish Peat Board) fleet of Ferguson and M-F tractors in Ireland. This is the fleet at just one of their peat harvesting locations.

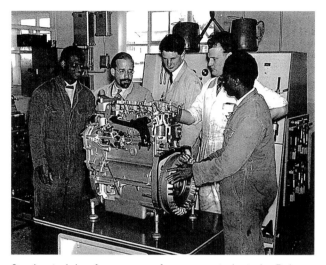

Service training for a group of overseas students by Bob (2nd from right) on the intricacies of an M-F 35 engine.

Bob (centre) in training mode with a group of students for the hydraulic systems of the MF 100 series tractors.

M-F demonstrations reached to all corners of the country in 1960! The start of a demonstration tour for the launch of the M-F 35 three cylinder tractor and the M-F Multi-Pull Hitch. Ralph Eagle left the British Road Service driver, Don Frampton 2nd from left the Senior Demonstrator, Dave Dennison Demonstrator 3rd from left and Phil Morley the Training Manager on the right. Other teams started off from different points in the UK..

A considerable amount of planning went into these events. Obviously tractors and implements would be decided, then it was ordering of lorries of acceptable sizes to transport plus ramps for off loading. Tractors matched to machines, wheel track settings adjusted, tyre specs and sizes checked, all set up in the field, then washed, cleaned, tractors fuelled, air cleaners checked, tyre pressures adjusted, oil levels checked etc, etc. Along with the equipment would be spare plough shares, cultivator tines, the spray kit, all necessary paint colours, thinners, spare decals, ploughing poles, measuring tapes, tools, jacks, cleaning rags, polish,

Demonstrating the M-F 711 Potato Harvester – the only such harvester ever made by M-F.

tyre paint, brushes, clean overalls, Belstaff Black Prince waterproof outfits, flag poles, white paint, flags, bunting, rope, the list was endless. In fact a major logistical operation!

We demonstrators would travel in Standard Vanguard pick-ups all in MF livery with public address systems fitted on the cab roof.

Once on site we would await the lorries, unload in all weathers and set to and prepare the site, creating plots, opening furrows, erecting flag poles etc, etc. It was just like the circus coming to town!

When the site was prepared it was back to the washing, cleaning and polishing, tractors would be parked always in perfect formation, in line, all gear levers in same position, three point linkage raised (no dangling lynch pins!). Tyres would be painted black, bonnets/hoods would be polished, all soil engaging parts anti-rusted and everything set up perfectly, the public address system checked out and final briefing for the team.

Every effort was made to have an eye catching, attention holding performance. One of the famous "party pieces" was – if the field allowed it – to have a tractor and plough appearing from over a brow of a hill ploughing a perfect furrow but without a driver! A team member would be at each end of the field and as the tractor and plough arrived he would mount it

and turn it round and send it back up over the hill to the other member who would turn it around and send it back again. This was first performed with the TE 20s and continued with the 35s. It should be remembered that in those days we did not use cabs at demonstrations. Where there were no hills it was quite common for the demonstrator to walk alongside the tractor talking to the farmer explaining the automatic draft control in operation. Nowadays such stunts would never be allowed due to Health and Safety rules and regulations.

Peter Delingpole was a consummate professional on the PA system. He was a natural as Ring Leader/Master of Ceremonies and should anything unexpected occur he could react immediately and salvage the situation and bring it round to our advantage! All of these public events were performed like a military tattoo, slick and crisp and well practised and it showed.

For a young person this was a wonderful job to have, learning about machinery, using it in all weathers, realising the importance of discipline and team-work and all this wrapped up in travelling around the country. Great! Later there were to be trips overseas as my role changed and came to include overseas training and service courses for which I show a few photographs here.

To the Forests

My first introduction to Forestry came in 1959/60 when I was an MF Demonstrator. As a department we used to attend and exhibit Forestry Exhibitions and Shows throughout the UK taking with us MF 35 and MF 65 tractors complete with half tracks, MF 704 winches, MF 723 post hole diggers, Swedish calliper grabs, timber sledges, Rosendingen timber trailers, sawbenches, single furrow disc ploughs, heavy duty offset disc harrows and plenty of front wheel weights!

I well remember going to somewhere near Crediton in Devon along with fellow demonstrator Peter Penrice to do a demonstration in a forest with what seemed to me to have near vertical hillsides!

I can still see and feel the almost terror at taking an MF 35 four cylinder tractor complete with half tracks and a Swedish logging trailer up these hills with the tractor resting backward on the "T" bar of the auto hitch in contact with the trailer drawbar. The front wheels, despite having inner and outer wheel weights, flapped in the air on the raised front axle, the half tracks just gripping their way up the hillside. It brought home the safety features built into the design of the automatic hitch and linkage. Steering was by use of the independent rear brakes. Coming down again was just a hair-raising experience using engine braking and wheel brakes to best advantage!

It followed on therefore that when I later became an instructor at Stoneleigh and had the opportunity in February 1962 to visit Sweden to conduct technical training on the MF 25 tractor plus MF 35 and 65 multipower on a nation-wide tour I took great interest in their forestry activities.

Sweden's equivalent to the Stoneleigh Training Centre was a large and very imposing country house called Hedenlunda, just outside the town of Myköping where the Swedish Distribution ANA had their head office. At Hedenlunda they held a full range of Swedish forestry equipment for training and demonstration purposes. The surrounding forest area showed off the true potential of this extensive range based on the 35 and 65 tractors.

As I moved north to Sundsvall and Skelleftea near the Arctic Circle I was able to see much of the equipment in daily commercial use in the countryside

An MF "Robur" Tractor in 1965 at Hedenlunda.

Logging near Sundsvall in the north of Sweden 1962.

The Ana Field School at Hedenlunda, Sweden 1962.

A Rotary Snow Plough on an M-F 65 Tractor near Hudiksvall.

Timber work near Hedenlunda in February 1962.

M-F 65 hauling logs in the north of Sweden 1962.

In the forest near Hedenlunda with a radio-controlled jib mounted on an M-F 65 with half tracks.

A demonstration of an M-F 25 Tractor at Skelleftea February 1962.

where temperatures were around the minus 25°C.

Again in February 1965 on another training visit, this time a service course on the MF 1100 tractor I had the chance to revisit Hedenlunda and saw how much the tractors and equipment had developed and become more specialised for forestry work. The Treever tractor and Robur units were examples of this.

Many of the cranes, jibs, and grabs were radio-controlled allowing the operator to load trailers and sledges whilst standing well clear, all very impressive to watch.

Up until this time MF had always been toying with the idea of going into forestry equipment but had only been prepared to supply tractors complete with front axles to companies who then removed them and fitted their own or created articulated machines. In around 1967-69 MF became more committed to this market and made available the yellow painted skid unit from the MF Industrial factory in Manchester.

A Caliper Grab for use with Ferguson Tractors was used for towing logs out of forests. It was marketed by M-F's Swedish agent Ana of Myköping.

The MF Demonstration Fleet Included:

10-15 MF 35 tractors of differing specifications and tyre sizes

6-8 MF 65 tractors of different specifications and tyre sizes

797 reversible plough – 2 F "N" bases

796 reversible plough – 1F "S" base

793 mouldboard ploughs – 10", 12", 16" spacing with "H", "N" and "Y" var point

765 disc plough for forestry demonstrations

723 subsoiler

722 mounted tandem disc harrows – 6 ft, 7 ft and 8 ft models

720 spring tine cultivators

738 tiller – 9, 11 and 13 tine

770 spike tooth harrows

728 ridger

721 spinner broadcaster

732 multipurpose seed drill

775 rear mounted mower

779 mid mounted mower

718 buckrake

721 multipurpose blade

723 post hole digger complete with 6", 9", 12" and 18" augers

704 linkage winch

FE 35 loaders

Tyre tracks fitted to 35

704 trailer

718 auto potato planter

717 3 ton trailers

Transport box

Link boxes.

This was the backbone of the fleet – any additional requirements were either borrowed from the Training Department fleet or brought in especially for the event.

Bob (centre) in the box! Demonstrating an M-F Pallet Tippler mounted on a Ferguson 35 Tractor. What would Health and Safety say about this type of activity now?!

Left, Above and Right: Three "in action" shots of the M-F Potato Harvester pulled by a Ferguson 35 Tractor. Bob to the right of the static shot adjusting or clearing the cleaning wheel.

Members of the MF Demonstration Team in Late 50s and Early 60s

Peter Delingpole – Manager
Dennis Langton – Assistant Manager
Dave Watkins
Nigel Liney
Dick Dowdeswell
Don Frampton
Guy Barton
Jim Edwards
Peter Penrice
Roger Gosling
Harley Robinson-Smith
Jeff Adams
Bob Gilchrist
Jack French

Finally, as there is such interest in the Ferguson LTX tractor I must place on record my only impression of it. I never drove it, but from a distance it was indistinguishable from the old TE-20s. However it was very distinguishable when you saw it raising a five furrow plough as it turned on a headland.

Instructor Bill Sargeant in white overalls came from the M-H camp. He is seen here demonstrating a South African made SAFIM Toolbar and Planter on a Tropical Agricultural Course at the Stoneleigh Training Centre.

The North Americans also had their spectacles. This is the line-up of tractor and equipment demonstrators for the Pageant of Profit.

Thousands of trainees passed through the gates of the M-F Training Centre to learn skills in the operation, maintenance and repair of farm machinery before it closed in 2005. The world-famous gates have now been scrapped. This shot was taken in 1987.

A Massey-Harris demonstration day thought to be at the Stoneleigh Training Centre. It shows the last British made M-H tractors – the 745 S models with truck type chassis (and which developed a reputation for breaking away from the transmission!); also a French made 820D with Hanomag diesel engine

Nigel Liney (see also page 123) on a Ferguson TEF tractor with Ferguson Buckrake clearing land on the Stoneleigh Deer Park which ultimately was part of the M-F Training Centre there.

From Father to Son (Canada, New Zealand, Rhodesia)

Leeroy Gordon

As you might expect I could write a book (in fact my father has!). He started with M-H in 1928 in S. Saskatchewan as an agent-dealer-blockman-regional branch manager, then subsequently became M-H Toronto King St. quality control supervisor in war years, the Brandon Manager, the Rhodesian Manager (1947-1953) and finally New Zealand Manager up to 1960 when he returned to the USA. From Rhodesia he was responsible for central Africa. From New Zealand he covered Borneo, Fiji and other remote locations. During the merger period he worked with C B Norwood, the Ferguson distributor in New Zealand where he oversaw the transition from the M-H branch/dealer system to Ferguson distributor system.

I began helping build M-H machinery as a lad in Rhodesia (late '40s) and New Zealand (mid '50s) and worked for the Implement Manufacturer P O Deecan in New Zealand. I graduated at the University of New Zealand in Agriculture and Agricultural Engineering and travelled in Australia and Europe, then did overseas training at Ferguson Stoneleigh Training Centre, Peterborough (Perkins Engines) and CAV Brighton (Fuel injection) then worked as an M-H Baler Serviceman at various locations in the UK in 1950. I gained a University of Toronto degree in Mechanical Engineering in 1961 and worked for MF Engineering in those years to finally gain permanent employment which lasted from 1958-1987. Subsequently I became North American Chief Test and Development Engineer at M-H King St in Toronto and at Brantford. Mostly I worked on combines – sometimes tractors, implements, swathers, chainsaws – you name it – and industrial equipment. We tested all over the world – Russia, China, Europe, Australia, Africa, North and South America. I also ran the MF Test Track at Melliken and the laboratories in town, finally retiring just before the death of M-F Combines!

You would have to understand the fundamental difference between traditional North American Farm Machinery companies and Ferguson organisation. No time to fully explain so please see the chart – Massey Harris was what we called floor planned and

had been so for 150 years! It differed fundamentally from the Ferguson organisation and this gave rise to some problems at the merger.

North American Organisation	Ferguson Organisation
Corporate – Engineering - Manufacturing ⬇ Head Office Distribution ⬇ Massey-Harris branches ⬇ Blockmen ⬇ Dealers + some associate agents ⬇ Customer	Engineering ⬇ Manufacturer ⬇ Wide area distributor ⬇ Agents ⬇ Customer

Leeroy Gordon spent quite some time working on M-H balers. Here we see the 701 Baler re-badged as an M-F 701 Baler. Note that it is pulled by a very early M-F 35 four cylinder diesel Tractor still bearing the Ferguson badge of the "grey-gold" Ferguson 35s.

My Hobby was my Job (USA)

Robert A Hadley

I am not equipped to do much in the way of literary contributions, so will do the best I can! I joined Harry Ferguson Inc. in 1946 as Staff Photographer in the office at Ford's Highland Park, Michigan plant. Ultimately I was to do advertising literature, sales promotion material, service and engineering manuals, and both production and prototype tractors and implements. Way on into Massey Ferguson days this was to include snowmobiles and clothing, and lawn and garden equipment. As a consequence of the merger harvesting equipment came into the frame. Most of the early work was still photos, but once every two years we would do a motion picture feature.

The merger of Ferguson and M-H had little effect, other than more work and more equipment. M-H didn't have a photography department so they were easy to please and work with. Most of the so-called prototypes eventually made it into production with but few changes. One notable item which never made it into production was a combination Snowmobile-Boat Combo. You could install tracks and skis for snow, or remove them and install an outboard motor for use on the water. The Japanese were interested but in the end they did not take it up.

Mr. Ferguson came to the USA several times. On one of his visits to the Ford offices he went in to the men's room. A young man was about ready to leave upon which Mr. Ferguson asked, "Young man don't you wash your hands before returning to work?" The young man replied, " I was not going to work sir, I was going to lunch"! It would have been good to capture this on film!!

Mr. Ferguson was a very proper gentleman and anyone caught with his hands in his pocket would be fined 10 cents on the spot, also he didn't like our fancy American men's ties!

I enjoyed being with Massey Ferguson a total of 34 years. My hobby was my job, and my job was my hobby. It had all started in the US 8th Air Force both in the UK for two years and two and a half years in the United States.

Demonstrating a Ferguson Tractor with Three Furrow Plough in the USA.

Another Robert Hadley shot, this time a Ferguson TO 20 Tractor with a full North American style lighting set.

Left to Right

Bill Nicholson, Lou Stienert, George Wildrick, Jack Moore, Owen Marshall, Don Gabiel,
Carl Ham, Gordon Mars, Mike Herderick, Ken Mortin, Ed Barrows

Showing off a Ferguson TO 20 Tractor at the Ferguson Service School – a Robert Hadley shot.

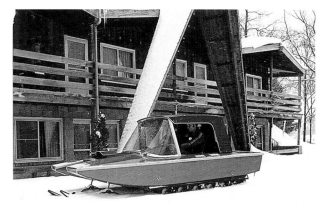

This spread: The M-F Snowmobile-
Boat Combo which apparently never
reached the market.

Farming with the LTX: a Lad's Recollections and Comparisons (UK)

Derek Hiatt

Derek Hiatt recalls that he was a young boy when his father's farm was used for testing the LTX tractors; he still farms the same farm. His childhood memories go back to Ford testing their new E27N Major in 1947. At the same time Ferguson men came along and asked to test the TE 20 with its new Standard Motor Co. engine. Derek's father offered them three fallow fields and they chose the worst, one with some steep slopes. Additionally the ground was very hard. His father told the Ferguson men that they wouldn't be able to do much. In the event the Ferguson, fitted with spade lugs, ploughed well – and up the slopes as well. Ford's couldn't even get their plough to penetrate!

Later the farm was used for extensive evaluation of the LTX prototypes or Ferguson 60s as they became known. Derek, still only a "lad" recalls that six or seven were built and generally there were three on the farm at any one time. They were routinely worked from 6 am till 10 pm by a team of drivers. Testing went on for 3-5 years. In spare time the tractors were used for scrub clearance where they had a very hard time of it. Trees were yanked out with a chain, the technique being to hitch the chain, then with the chain still slack roar off in second gear. But the LTX was up to the task. Derek recalls that the Ferguson test drivers gave the LTXs some pretty hard treatment in general.

Some of the LTX's had petrol engines, the others diesel. Derek particularly recalls the excellent lugging characteristics and power of the diesel. He thinks both were rated at about 60 hp – bigger than anything else available at the time. He believes that it would have swept the market had it been introduced in a timely manner and probably taken the like of Ford ten years to catch up with. All the tractors that came to the farm had the same style bodies.

One tractor was to stay on the farm for many years after the others had been scrapped. Derek recalls it being a very well balanced tractor which in all respects drove and felt simply like a big TE 20 Ferguson. He only recalls two problems. Firstly it could be a slow starter in cold weather and the engineers used to light a small fire under the inlet manifold to overcome the

problem. Secondly they used to jump out of second gear but Ferguson improvisation in the field solved this by wedging a Ferguson spanner between the gear lever and steering column. Later the problem was identified as having been caused by the severe stress of tree snatching! The one that stayed eventually required a new clutch – but that would seem to be fair wear and tear! The differential lock was hand operated and had to be manually disengaged unlike the later designs which released when the foot pedal actuator was released. The LTX "fixed in" type of differential lock would not have been acceptable under later safety legislation. The fate of the one tractor that stayed on the farm was a sad one. It was sent back to the factory for repair after many years. There it was "seized" as a missing prototype and scrapped!

LTX tractor testing was undertaken with some prototype Ferguson implements. These included 4 and 5 furrow ploughs – the 5th furrow was attached or detached as required, a 13 tine spring cultivator with beefed up frame, a set of Ferguson type discs (he thinks possibly with more discs); and a large, low, two wheel tipping trailer which used a conventional style Ferguson pick up hitch. This trailer had fixed outward sloping sides with the wheels sitting outside the body. Derek feels that the trailer would not have been readily accepted because of the wheel position.

Derek has the unique experience of being able to compare the LTX with the Ferguson 35 and Massey Ferguson 65 under farm conditions, because the family went on to use these later models. He gives much praise to the 35 design, but adamantly declares that the 65 was just no match for the LTX. In fact he regards the 65 being "two furrow inferior" and having nothing like the balanced operational design of the LTX.

The closing words from Derek: "A crying shame that the LTX was scrapped!"

This LTX Ferguson prototype Tractor is believed to be the one which stayed on Derek Hiatt's farm due to the fact that it had a cab fitted. Believed to be a petrol engine model. Note also the use of wheel girdles. © Nigel Liney.

Put a Boy in the Baler Tool Box (UK)

Brian Johnson

On parade at M-H's Barton Dock Road plant an M-H 726 Combine which was the backbone of M-H's combine assault on the UK's harvest fields. Harvesting equipment was M-H's major strength in field machinery which Ferguson did not have. In the background is an M-H 744D tractor, a derivative of M-H's American made M-H 44. The UK's first M-H combine (M-H 722) and first M-H tractor (M-H 744 PD) were made at Manchester before their production was transferred to Kilmarnock.

Although now almost half a century ago, my recollection of the merger is very clear indeed. In 1953 the Royal Show was at Blackpool and the Massey-Harris and Harry Ferguson stands were situated side by side. As competitors in the farm machinery market it would be difficult to have found a greater contrast.

Having joined M-H in 1948 at the age of twenty (after two years National Service in the Army) I was a junior member of field staff on stand duty. Late in the afternoon of the second or third day of the show, the news vendor came round with copies of the evening paper bearing the shock headline "Massey Harris and Ferguson Merger" or some similar words blazoned across the front page.

Despite the months of negotiations which must have preceded their announcement, it was the first any of us had heard of such a momentous event. Gradually as the fact began to sink in, and as sheer disbelief gave way to apprehension, one or two brave souls crossed the dividing aisle from either side and tentatively shook hands with their opposite number on the adjacent stand.

We had gone into the show as such rivals and suddenly were to become one family. As we left the

SPECIAL COURSE No. 9, FERGUSON FOR MASSEY-HARRIS PERSONNEL—25th to 27th JANUARY, 1954.
Back Row, Left to Right—MR. DREWES, MR. J. HALE, MR. HRAB, MR. D. W. McDIARMID (Instructor), MR. EAMES, MR. BUYS, MR. LI. GRIFFITH JONES (Instructor), MR. W. MOESER, MR. FLOHIMONT.
Front Row, Left to Right—MR. N. PROVEN, MR. B. JOHNSON, MR. BLOOD, MR. MORTON, MR. GRANT.

Brian Johnson (front 2nd from left) receiving instruction in Ferguson matters at the Ferguson School of Farm Mechanisation at Stoneleigh.

showground that evening we wondered just what the future held – job prospects, promotion, re-organisation, possibly redundancy? One thing was certain, our lives would never be the same again.

Training

Towards the end of the year, two other colleagues and I were sent to Stoneleigh as M-H instructors at the renowned Ferguson School of Farm Mechanisation. Here courses were to be held to indoctrinate the staff of both companies and later, their respective dealer networks. Students from around the world flocked here like pilgrims to Mecca to worship at the shrine of the Harry Ferguson System.

The School was run with military precision under the ever watchful eye of the redoubtable Captain D. C. Hill, D.S.O., R.N. Retired. By 8.30 each morning neat rows of grey Standard Vanguard vans in Ferguson livery were lined up outside the training buildings. Until our arrival in our bright red Austin A40 vans, "Pioneers of Farm Mechanisation" proudly displayed on their sides, nothing had spoilt the harmony of grey vehicles, grey TE 20s and grey implements neatly arrayed. How the Captain (or Admiral as he was better known) hated the sight of us intruders when on his daily rounds of inspection!

Only Two Threads

One of Harry Ferguson's golden rules was that in any assembly of components there should never be more than two threads of a bolt protruding beyond its nut. This undoubtedly contributed to Ferguson's characteristically neat looking products. When instructing groups of Ferguson executives and staff I will always remember their expressions of horror and near disbelief as they critically viewed such M-H machines as our 712 Muck Spreader, 717 Fertiliser Distributor and 744D tractor all with bolts proudly protruding. I was obliged to explain that our factories would never have been able to put these fine machines together without bolts that were long enough to line up the various assemblies!

This rather highlighted the gulf between the heritage of the two companies. Massey-Harris had partly evolved from Daniel Massey's blacksmith shop in Canada while Ferguson's machines owed more to the motor and aircraft industries with which Harry Ferguson had been associated. On such occasions I found it difficult not to remind the "men in grey suits" that it was, after all, Massey-Harris who had in effect taken over Ferguson and not vice versa as it so often appeared. But any such comment would have done little to undermine the distinct air of superiority which emanated from the Ferguson camp.

Nearing the end! Brian took this photo of an M-H 34 Mower at Warminster, Wiltshire in 1948. A successful machine in its day but just one of the M-H heavy implement designs that would subsequently be abandoned with the advent of the merger and acquisition of Ferguson's advanced engineering prowess.

The M-H 55K being driven leisurely through Stoneleigh Park. The 55K was at one time the biggest tractor available to world farmers. The K designated that it was a kerosene (tvo) model.

Bring on the 55K

A message that there was need to impress these "little toy tractor men" must have got back to the M-H moguls in Toronto as our tenuous presence at Stoneleigh was soon bolstered by the arrival of a shipment of some heavyweight monsters from the red range.

On one occasion I found myself having to demonstrate the raw power of a 55K tractor (whose front wheels were more or less the same size as TE 20's rears), by towing a huge multi-tine cultivator called a Trash King and whose main function was busting the endless acres of prairie stubble in the American wheat belt. Of course this combination was totally unsuited to UK conditions especially the well-tilled demo plots on the Stoneleigh estate.

I had been told to drive this ungainly rig at high speed so as to impress our visiting students. After a couple of high speed passes, the hitch pin must have jumped out and for a few yards I was towing the Trash King by the hydraulic pipe which operated its slave ram. Needless to say the hose snapped and I was covered in confusion and hot hydraulic fluid. As luck would have it the student group had just turned away to view an adjacent demo and were unaware of the mayhem behind them!

On another occasion I was test driving a prototype 745 tractor with a cast front axle mounting. Suddenly the tractor nose-dived into a slit trench which had been concealed beneath the bracken growth ever since the second world war. When we hauled the tractor out we found that the front casting had cracked. Fearing a serious reprimand, I reported the incident to Pat Mulholland, the M-H tractor engineer. To my surprise and relief he thanked me for succeeding where months of rig-testing had failed thus persuading him to adopt a pressed steel design for subsequent production.

The Baler with a Boy

The M-H Trash King Cultivator pulled by the M-H 55K Tractor.

My other most significant product recollections of the Massey days mainly concerned the 701 Baler. This machine was introduced in the early 1950s and only survived after a major re-conditioning programme in which the entire first two years' production was taken back to the Manchester and Kilmarnock factories and completely rebuilt with many modified components, at no cost to the customer. Many of the problems were concerned with the tripping and bale-tying mechanisms. This resulted in bales which were either of double length, half size or not tied at all.

In the field we were at our wits' end to rectify the problems and many and strange were the remedies suggested. In our area in the south-west of England, we found after the season that we had been called out to every machine except one and decided that herein lay the answer to all our troubles. Accordingly we dashed off to visit the owner, a contractor in Somerset who expressed himself so delighted with his baler that he intended ordering a second machine for the following season. Our plan was to engage him in conversation while the third member of our team surreptitiously crawled all over and under the machine in its winter shed. After more than an hour of fruitless

inspection, we were about to take our leave when a little lad trotted into the yard. "Here, he'll tell you about the baler," said the farmer. We listened intently while they described how the boy, his grandson, had sat on the back of the bale chamber throughout the season and had quite happily tied every single loose bale by hand! Our subsequent report to the factory recommended that the only solution was to supply a small boy in every toolbox!

Merging the Networks

In the 1960s and several reorganisations later, I was involved in merging the two distribution networks. Prior to the merger M-H had some 750 dealers/distributors and Ferguson about two hundred throughout the UK. As the two product lines were progressively merged into a single franchise, the lengthy and often acrimonious process of "rationalisation" progressed, until by the 1970s there were some two hundred and fifty distributors for the now fully integrated M-F range of products.

Above: The French also had to merge Ferguson and M-H interests. An advertising leaflet for a French dealership.

Right: The M-H 701 Baler immortalised in an oil painting by esteemed transport artist Terence Cuneo who was commissioned by M-H in 1951.

Ferguson: Specialists and Organisation (Canada)

Harold Jonah

I started with M-H in 1951 and was with the Ontario Sales Branch from 1951-1982. I worked in several different departments, but mostly as a Field Service Representative, Service Manager and Service Training Manager.

Ferguson Sales and Service in Ontario was handled by a distributor – Truck and Tractor Inc. located in Mississauga. With the 1953 merger, many of Truck and Tractor employees were absorbed into the M-H organisation. For the first two years the company maintained the "Red line and Grey line" as separate dealer organisations, but they were serviced by the same personnel. The Ferguson factory and head office was in Detroit in the U.S.A and therefore out of Toronto.

One thing that stands out in my memory was that with Ferguson everything was well organised. There were plans and procedures for everything such as safe presentation and field presentations. At the time of the merger in 1953 I was in the Field Service

department and we were responsible for exhibits and demonstrations as well. We had to service both the red and grey lines impartially! The main objective during the M-H-F period was getting across to the dealer organisation the principles of the Ferguson hydraulic three point hitch system and how to service and repair it.

Ferguson had specialists in every segment of the organisation. In the summer they would organise evening field demonstrations and presentations in farmers' fields. They had tents, electric generating, lights, PA speakers and written procedures to follow. Then there were the fall fairs, ploughing matches and private customer demonstrations.

In the M-H-F period the company purchased several small manufacturing companies – some of which didn't prove worthwhile. Examples of these were the Goble disc, the hay pelleting machine, the model 60 forage harvester and others.

Some towns had both Ferguson and Massey-Harris dealers and there was great rivalry. Dealerships in those days tended to be small and located within 25 miles of each other. After the introduction of the Ferguson TO 35 tractor the best performing dealerships were amalgamated.

The Ferguson side mounted baler and forage harvester were well made machines but unfortunately gave a lot of trouble. They were discontinued, taken back from farmers and scrapped. One customer I knew refused to give up his forage harvester in spite of all the trouble he had with it and used it for several more years.

Above: Demonstrating the new M-F Tractors.

Left: From the grey stable but red! and a breakthrough. The M-H 50 Tractor was a Ferguson System Tractor made to placate North American M-H dealers requirement for a Ferguson System Tractor. It was offered in four types of wheel configurations – standard, rowcrop, V twin front tricycle rowcrop and single front tricycle rowcrop as shown here. Harry Ferguson had always opposed tricycle type tractors but with this model the mould was broken and for the first time a Ferguson System Tractor was a tricycle.

Experiencing the LTX Tractor – and More (UK)

Nigel Liney

Nigel joined Harry Ferguson in 1950 and spent 42 years with Ferguson, Massey-Harris-Ferguson and then Massey Ferguson. He recalls:

The LTX tractor (Ferguson 60)

I worked with all the usual TE 20 models and many good implements that never saw production, not because they were no good, far from it, many were excellent, but if Harry Ferguson did not like them – out they would go.

I was one of the few who worked with the LTX tractor all night and all day and in all weathers. What a machine, nothing would beat it, all others Ford, Nuffield, International, David Brown, you name it, we could leave them standing. The few of us were entirely sold on this machine and looked forward to simply slaughtering the opposition when in production.

You know the story. Massey-Harris did not believe its performance even when seen with their own eyes. North American engineering said it must have a tricycle undercarriage, which would have been very easy and a few other alterations. Harry Ferguson said no way, the North American politics said we would have the 35 tractor – scrap the LTX.

By this time the production model was finished and enough engines etc. ready for the word go. Those of us in engineering were shattered. The biggest mistake any major company could and did make. Then to join with Massey-Harris who made a tractor out of the ark, being only good for the third world countries.

It was like saying to Mr. Edison, sorry we don't like your light bulb, you will have to join with Valor and make oil lamps.

No we did not like joining with M-H and for many years there was that divide between us but we eventually worked well together.

What happened to the LTX? Well all the drawings were thrown away, all the pre-production machines and parts cut up onto the scrap heap. One tractor escaped, being left on a farm. However, the farmer after many years asked the company to replace the clutch as it was worn, so they took it back and quickly cut it up. He has kicked himself ever since as it would be worth a fortune today.

Why was the LTX so good? What a question the author asked! To be quite honest I don't know, having driven it in all conditions possible in the field and on the roads. All I can tell you is that you would have to experience the machine yourself to understand its superb performance. This was undoubtedly achieved with the outstanding engine which had all the power we needed, fantastic torque back up and superb hydraulics using the three piston pump, plus the differential lock being in constant use in difficult conditions when ploughing. You did have to remember to disengage the differential at the end of a run unless you wanted to go through the hedge!

An in-field, dirty tyres photo of one of the LTX tractors.

Nigel ploughing on steep slopes with an MF 35 Tractor.

One of the Ferguson TO 35s from the USA on trial in Warwickshire with a Ferguson Side-mounted Forage Harvester. Note that it has P.A.V.T. wheels. The forager has a Ferguson Power Unit mounted on it to provide power to it instead of the alternative pto drive arrangement.

M-H wall posters and demonstration units of the Ferguson TE Tractor rear end and engine demonstrate the gradual fusion of activities at the Stoneleigh School of Farm Mechanisation. It evolved to be the M-F Training Centre

Nigel with a Ferguson TE Tractor coupled to a Ferguson Polydisc Seeder and Cultivator. Note the mix of Ferguson and M-H tractors and equipment that came to be assembled at Stoneleigh.

Other Tractors and Implements

Nigel was lucky enough to drive the first TO 35 tractor brought over from the U.S.A. for familiarisation of U.K. staff. He vividly remembers the steering wheel coming off in his hands!

He also recalls trials of fitting Meadows four cylinder diesel engines into TE 20 Fergusons. One or two were so fitted for evaluation, but they were never adopted for production. Nigel has a single photograph of such a tractor, but it is sadly of very poor quality.

Nigel didn't like the Ferguson manure spreader. A certain cog wore out very quickly. One day Harry Ferguson asked him what he thought of the spreader. Nigel was to the point! Harry Ferguson walked off, there was no comeback on Nigel; but he suspects that someone in the engineering drawing office may have fared less well!

He was also involved with testing a French-made Ferguson side-mounted mower and describes it as an awful machine with bearings always running hot. It never reached the market.

A recollection on the M-H side is that inertia starters were fitted to many M-H 744 and 745 tractors which were sent out to Africa. These are starters which are cranked up by hand, so "winding up" a spring. When this is complete, the spring is manually tripped and all the stored energy in the spring is instantly released to crank the engine very successfully.

Author's note. I can vouch for the efficiency of these inertia starters having fitted them to MF 35 four cylinder diesel tractors in Saudi Arabia. They were the boss of that wretched 23C engine!

A fine line-up of M-H and Ferguson machines at Stoneleigh.

Heavy North American made M-H cultivation equipment was brought to The Stoneleigh School for evaluation for British conditions and possible use in the British Colonial territories. In the foreground is an M-H Goble Disc Harrow and behind it a Multi Disc Plow.

Combines, Balers and a Bucket Full of Parts

With my experience with the Ferguson wrap-around combine I found myself at The School of Farm Mechanisation at Stoneleigh as a trainee technical instructor on combines. This of course brought me onto the Massey-Harris side of the business. This gave me a unique opportunity to integrate myself into the best side of Massey-Harris who at that time harvested more grain in this country and North America than any other manufacturer. Whilst testing the Ferguson machine a Massey-Harris 735 was alongside us for comparison, so the integration of personnel really began at this stage.

I personally found the technical side of combines fascinating but where the combine differed from tractors was in the field. Not only do you need to know how the mechanics work but how to set it to produce a good sample in all conditions and crops.

We had an M-H 735 combine on trial in the Cotswolds while testing the Ferguson side mounted combines. As far as I can remember it performed

well, the only trouble the Massey driver had was that the engine would keep switching itself off after only twenty minutes running. It drove the driver mad as he tried all the usual checks, until he found that the ignition key rattled itself into the off position without him noticing. The engine was the old Austin A 40.

A tanker version of a British built Ferguson Side-mounted Combine. Note that it is mounted on a USA built Ferguson TO 35 Tractor.

Arnold Shepherd on Ferguson TEF Tractor pulling an M-H 750 Combine at the Stoneleigh School of Farm Mechanisation.

An M-H 55K with four furrow Disc Plough at work on the Stoneleigh School of Farm Mechanisation.

I was involved with the 735 and 780 combines and the 703 baler. I ran courses on all of these at the Stoneleigh School as an instructor. They were good machines but the outputs were starting to lag behind the opposition. On the courses we would strip the machines down and if in season take them into the field to prove they still worked after such treatment. In the summer we would backup our Service Department and travel to all machines giving trouble, either in the U.K. or overseas. I was once presented with a bucket full of baler knotter parts in Persia and asked if I would please put it together!

One of the British built Ferguson Side-mounted Combines on trial in the Cotswolds.

The French Ferguson combine

My only experience of this machine was to drive it through Coventry in the morning rush hour to deliver it for shipping. French engineering had cut the TE 20 in half, the engine being removed from the bell housing and fitted crossways at the rear. The driver sat on the rear half which gave him a good view of the table. The time to remove the working parts and restore the tractor would be a major operation and beyond the capability of any small farmer, unlike the twenty or fifteen minutes with the U.K. Ferguson design combine. All I can tell you of this machine is that with the steering wheels at the back, and the steering wheel working in reverse (turn right and you turned left), it was hair raising to me!

I think this is where I must leave you as I never left the combine side for the rest of my 42 years travelling round the world in about 43 countries so you could say this was one man who, although a strong Harry Ferguson man, was totally integrated into Massey with Ferguson.

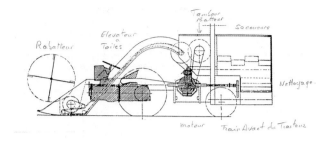

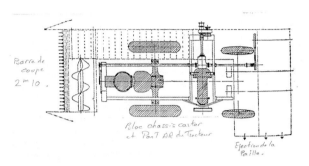

Above: Working shot and two sectional diagrams of the French Ferguson Combine Harvester. The tractor had to be completely split in half with the engine unit placed crosswise across the whole unit.

Left: A French built M-H 90 (890) Combine on Rice Tracks under evaluation at the Stoneleigh School of Farm Mechanisation.

South Africa Assignment – First Class and Armed! (South Africa)

Robin H Litton

I joined Harry Ferguson Ltd. at the beginning of 1952 with the expectation of eventually going to one of the overseas companies, though I never knew when or where I would be sent until July 1953 when I was told I would be joining the staff of Harry Ferguson of South Africa Ltd. In the meantime, I with other Export Department trainees, started life at the Education Department at Stoneleigh Abbey. It was a good grounding, though at the time I did feel that I was getting brain washed into believing that there was nothing to beat a Ferguson tractor and implements. It stayed with me all my life! Shortly before I sailed to South Africa in August 1953 the merger of Massey-Harris and Ferguson took place. It came completely out of the blue. We were naturally a little concerned but told not to worry as no major changes would take place for some time. In fact no changes took place in South Africa until after I left the company in 1956.

Harry Ferguson employees always travelled First Class and so it was for me on the Union Castle liner "Athlone Castle" to Durban. I was met in Cape Town by Jamie Strydom, the Ferguson agent there. There were six staff in Durban and two more based in Nairobi. Between us we were responsible for southern, central and east Africa. Needless to say we had some interesting trips!

Getting Started

One of the first pieces of advice I received was to carry a .32 Colt. It was the time of the Mau Mau

troubles. This I did but I never had to use it. I was given the grand title of Education Executive but most of my work was in the offices and out in the field trouble-shooting, dealing with warranty claims and education. Tractors and Farm Tools Ltd, our excellent South African distributors had a modern farm school at Richmond loosely based on the Ferguson School at Stoneleigh. We also got involved in sales promotion and demonstrations aimed at government buying agencies in conjunction with our agents and dealers in various countries. Because I had served an apprenticeship in agricultural engineering I also became involved with the selection of drawings and specifications of implements from Harry Ferguson companies and their suppliers around the world – mostly Harry Ferguson Inc. in the USA. We needed to manufacture Ferguson implements locally to save on foreign exchange.

S.A.F.I.M.

I also visited S.A.F.I.M. (South African Farm Implement Manufacturers) at Vereeniging, Transvaal who were owned by Massey-Harris. Some steel specifications had to be changed on our drawings to suit the available South African steel – we always erred on the side of strength. I well remember a batch of disc ploughs which we received from S.A.F.I.M. They could not be assembled. The night shift welders had got drunk and welded the tubular frames with the discs up in the air!

An example of an implement made by S.A.F.I.M. locally to complement the Ferguson range.

A S.A.F.I.M. style tractor plough made for the M-H range and special conditions of South Africa.

THE *Ferguson*
DIESEL TRACTOR

EASILY STARTED IN COLD WEATHER

INCORPORATES ALL THE FEATURES OF THE FERGUSON SYSTEM

DEVELOPS 25 BELT HORSE POWER

SPECIFICATION

The Ferguson Tractor that suffered the dust. Note the low position of the air cleaner inlet pulling dust up off the front wheel. Robin fixed it!

Fun and Games

Sons of dealers were sent to Stoneleigh ostensibly for training but in fact having a good time away from their fathers. I competed in the Daily Express 1220 mile round Britain rally with one and against such competition as Stirling Moss. One had to bring the dealers into the family!

Once we were called to an Agricultural College because a Ferguson tractor was blocking the entrance doorway. The students had driven it in. It just went in on the 48 in. wheel setting, but then they had widened the front axle to 52 in. and one could only enter the College by climbing over it.

TEF Diesel Tractors

Tractors and Farm Tools had delayed having the TEF tractors for some time, but they were getting into neighbouring countries and customers wanted to buy them. The dealers had mixed feelings because of the cost of the additional special tools they were expected to buy. It was always a sore point. In 1954 some TEFs came into the country and went to a number of dealers and their selected customers to try out. In order to make them look more powerful than the TEAs and TEDs (which they weren't) they were fitted with 11 x 28 rear and 6 x 16 front tyres. At 4000 feet up on the High Veldt they showed a considerable power loss. The fuel injection pumps had to be re-calibrated. Just when I thought I had the

problem overcome another one appeared. Dealers were reporting massive amounts of wear in the TEF engines. The mechanics were amazed at the oval bores! I had never seen any wear like it. We rebuilt engines but they were as bad as ever a week later. We decided that the problem was the abrasive dust coming straight up off the front wheel into the air cleaner. So we designed a long upswept air intake pipe with the centrifugal pre-cleaner on the top, and with regular washing of the oil bath cleaner the problem was solved.

I made the mistake of advising the Service Department in Coventry in case other countries might be able to benefit. I was promptly reprimanded for not getting permission from Harry Ferguson Engineering for a modification. Nobody likes a smart guy! The device seemed so vital that we carried on and ignored Coventry. Two years later I received a letter from M-H-F in Coventry with a drawing of an upswept air intake looking just like ours, made by Harry Ferguson in India. The writer said he hoped it might solve our problems in Africa!

On Leaving.......

I couldn't take the Colt home with me to the U.K. So I took it to the bank in Durban to place it in a deposit box. I put it on the counter. The bank teller thought it was a hold-up and pressed the alarm bell. All hell was let loose!

The Origins of MF in South Africa (South Africa)

J P A Maitre

Extract from an article written by J P A Maitre, Hon-Vice President, The Association of Massey Ferguson Dealers in South Africa:

Massey-Harris's presence in South Africa began in the 1880s. The commercial house R.M. Ross and Co. of Cape Town became distributors for the reapers and binders. Subsequently other distributors were appointed, although Ross & Co. remained as chief agents.

In 1925 Massey Harris decided to open a branch office at Durban. In December Massey Harris formed its first local company, Massey Harris (South Africa) (Pty) Ltd. Subsequently depots were opened in Johannesburg and East London. When Ross and Co. went out of existence in 1931, Massey Harris succeeded them in the Cape. Further branches were opened at Salisbury and Nakuru, Kenya.

During the second world war, supply of imports dwindled ominously, this caused Lt Col K. Rood, who was then chairman of the Union Steel Corporation, to embark on the local manufacturing of implements. S.A.F.I.M. (South African Farm Implement Manufacturers) was created at the end of 1939 and soon became the largest local manufacturer of implements. The venture was backed financially by Federale Volksbeleggings and Champion Ltd of Bloemfontein.

S.A.F.I.M. specialised in the manufacture of animal drawn implements, but lacked the expertise to manufacture tractor-drawn implements. Col. Rood approached Massey Harris with the result that MH acquired a 20% share in S.A.F.I.M. which at the time was managed by Dr Kusc.

Massey Harris bought part of Federale shareholding, eventually gaining control of S.A.F.I.M. with a 52% shareholding in 1952. In 1960 control of Champions was acquired and M-H owned the bulk of S.A.F.I.M.

In 1947 the late Mr Justin McCarthy, Chairman of the McCarthy Rodway Group, together with Mr

"SAFIM/MASSEY-HARRIS" THE NAME OF QUALITY

The S.A.F.I.M. factory from one of their late 1950s catalogues.

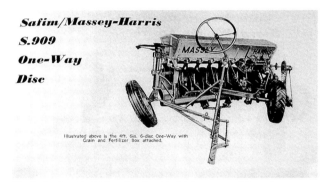

Safim/Massey-Harris S.909 One-Way Disc

Illustrated above is the 4ft. 6in. 6-disc One-Way with Grain and Fertilizer Box attached.

Made in South Africa for South African conditions by SAFIM/Massey-Harris. This 909 One Way Seeder is shown in a 1957 catalogue.

Two examples of machines made locally by S.A.F.I.M. for the Ferguson and M-F Tractors.

D.L. Vodermann successfully applied for the national representation of Ferguson Tractors in South Africa. There were some eighty applicants for the franchise.

A company called Tractors and Farm Tools (TAFT) was subsequently floated and listed on the Johannesburg Stock Exchange in 1949 with an issued share capital of £300,000.00. McCarthy Rodway were the largest shareholders with 25% of the equity. There were some three hundred shareholders in all. The Directors were J.B. McCarthy (Chairman), L.A. Brazier, F.V. Evans, J.P.W. Howden and P.J. McCarthy.

The management team known to the writer were as follows:

D.L. Vodermann (USA)	General Manager
J.R. McCarthy C.A. (S.A.)	Secretary and Financial Manager
Boet van Niekerk	Manager
Ben Johnson	Sales Manager
Dick Southey, Ian Gillies, Piet Stoffberg & others	District Managers
B.Badenhorst	Training Manager
Arie Weeda	Engineering Specialist
Angus Bowness	Service Manager
Rex Alexander	Spares Manager
Jim O'Niel	Farm manager

The small grey petrol and paraffin tractors were an immediate success with the South African Farming Community and sales were only limited by the availability of import permits in the early years (1948 to 1954). Sales averaged about two hundred units a month in the period to 1954 but increased substantially when the diesel version was introduced, followed in 1956 by the FE 35 models in paraffin and diesel versions.

A model farm school was created true to the Harry Ferguson mould. The farm Lincoln in the Richmond district of Natal was purchased, new buildings designed to incorporate lecture rooms, dining room, lounge, bedrooms to accommodate the students, etc. were built. The training received was excellent and all of us who attended courses at Lincoln knew just about all there was to know about the Ferguson System. We were far better trained than our competitors.

After the merger of Massey Harris and Harry Ferguson, separate representation continued. However as TAFT was a success history, and in line with MF policy of moving towards one product line, the entire franchise was consolidated under the TAFT banner in 1957.

On the 1st of November 1957 Malcomess were given the franchise for harvesting equipment and trailed implements followed by the Landini tractor franchise after MF acquired Landini of Fabrica Italy.

The introduction of the MF35X and the MF65 tractors had a further impact on sales and MF became

Quite a few vineyard versions of the M-F 35 Tractor as petrol/tvo or diesel types went down to South Africa for use in orchards and vineyards.

market leaders.

In 1960, in line with MF intention of handling their own distribution, Messrs. Varity, Shiner, Mawhinney and Reeth from MF Toronto visited South Africa. Tractor and Farm Tools was purchased on a friendly take over basis for R 2 000 000.00. The distribution agreement for harvesting and trailed implements with Malcomess was terminated and the MF head office was located at SAFIM Vereeniging under the management of Dr L.B. Knoll.

The consolidation of the various businesses under one roof initially resulted in chaos. However order was quickly restored, greater efficiency achieved and the MF tractor and implement range remained market leaders. In 1963 almost one out of every two tractors sold in South Africa was a Massey Ferguson.

The executives at Massey Ferguson S.A. Ltd were as follows:

Dr L.B. Knoll	Managing Director
Dick Harris (USA)	Director of Marketing
Ben Johnson	Sales Manager
Floris Brandt	Comptroller
Jan le Grange	Director Planning & Procurement
Bill Drennan	Publicity, Advertising and Public Relation
Geoff Metcalfe (UK)	Service Manager
Lawne Schroeder	Manager, Cape Town

Branch

Plus a team of district managers made up of some outstanding people.

The writer worked closely with Les Pearce and the late Peter Stoffberg.

Ferguson ran a tractor rebuild service in South Africa called the "Silver Star".

The Oldest of Recollections (Canada)

"Purc" McMaster

It has been a privilege to use the recollections of "Purc" McMaster. At 98 he it the oldest to contribute to this book. The following is taken partly from a book he prepared – "Purcell McMaster Memoirs from 1905. From Homesteading to a Lifetime of Service with Massey-Harris" – and partly from answers to specific questions which I posed through his friends George and Barb Smyth of Ontario.

Purc started his M-H career with M-H and Chevrolet dealers Huike and Fisher Motors in Shaunavon, Sasaktchewan in 1936 after the failure of his home farms in the depression. He was subsequently offered a job in the M-H Regina branch – the start of his employment by M-H. By the time of the merger he was the Service Manager for the Industrial Division in Canada with direct contact with Mid-Western Industries in Witchita, Kansas. He had been authorised a "short-cut" route to them to avoid delays of going through M-H procedures. At the merger he was given an assistant, Bill Staavert from Bombardier, the Montreal Ferguson dealer. He knew all the Ferguson dealers - and their good and bad points! Most were "crying" about M-H having 7 or 8 tractors whilst they only had one. Bill used to present dealers with "Cry Towels" saying get this over with, then we can talk business. Very few Ferguson dealers seemed interested in the new M-H-F company. It was a difficult time as some of the old Ferguson people kept telling the M-H people that they were going to be modernised.

One of the first big programmes was to set up a Dealer Service Training Programme under General Services headed by Joe Zimmerman. This failed and Purc, who had a massive reputation as a hands on trouble-shooter and organiser was called to return from Calgary (where he was demonstrating a radio-controlled M-H 33) to Toronto. He then went with Zimmerman to Detroit where he found there to be little or no organisation to the programme. He

Above: Ferguson ran a tractor rebuild service in South Africa called the "Silver Star".

Left: A fine effort from an nonagenarian. Lots of tales of events in old M-H days, the book is still available.

stayed for a couple of days to appoint two supervisors to evaluate the programme and then was again summoned by Zimmerman to London, Ontario. The bomb then dropped as Purc puts it! Purc was put in full charge of the USA M-H-F Service and Service Training Programme. The programme was to be put on an urgent schedule in order that Al Thornbrough could launch it as announced.

At the merger, Ferguson personnel had had their employment protected. To get the programme under way Purc had to dismiss a few and they were duly compensated as a charge to the Training Programme. The Service Department was duly reorganised and Don Potter became US Service Manager.

Purc recalls that the Detroit tractor factory was controlled by Ferguson people and he felt somewhat unwelcome there when he was presenting arising field problems. One big problem was gumming of fuel in the carburettors. Purc traced it to be a quality problem and the gasoline supplier to the factory was changed.

Purc also recalls that the five Canadian Western Branch Managers were having good sales campaigns with the M-H 22-55 tractor range, and also the M-H 90 and 92 combines. They became concerned when Herbert Klemm, the Chief Ferguson Engineer (of TO 35 fame), started eliminating the "practical" M-H engineers and started to push the aircraft type "smooth" ideas" into the agricultural and industrial arenas.

In 1960 a map was prepared of North American Dealer locations to determine a central location in the USA for a service training location. Terra Haute in Indianapolis was selected as a favourable and central location. There were no facilities in that town but 70 miles away in Indianapolis was a Massey Harris Branch building which was closed as a Branch Sales Office and only used as a parts distribution centre. That building was available and was selected as the location for the Training Centre. A plan was prepared with a capacity to handle 125 students. It was opened in November 1961 with a Branch Service meeting of over 100 dealers. Ferguson people from Detroit joined the staff in Terra Haute. Advice on the management structure was also taken from the UK Training School in Coventry who sent a man over to study and report. Out of that came a recommendation for a third manager.

Some Ferguson people who wanted Product Field Training included at a favourable local location felt that the Service Training would dominate over the Product Training. L. Pomeroy from head office, invited the Head of the Ferguson Product Training in the U.K. to look us over and advise. This resulted in a Ferguson man – John Hooker- being put in charge of both sections.

The M-H 22 Tractor was released after the war and derived successively from the wartime M-H 81, then post-war M-H 20 tractors. It was a popular small farm tractor in North America available in standard and rowcrop configurations. This example is owned by the author's son and being driven by one of the UK's leading M-H enthusiasts Malcolm Robinson.

Sent to Coventry (Scotland and England)

Alex McMillan

My first contact with Massey-Harris was on the 11th November, 1949 at Moorfield Industrial Estate, Kilmarnock where I went to apply for a job. When I arrived I was greeted with the sound of Glasgow Police Pipe Band and thought, "Well, I didn't expect such a welcome as this." However, although the factory had been in production for some months before, this was the official opening ceremony attended by the Massey-Harris hierarchy and the local dignitaries. After the ceremony the workers were given the afternoon off and an extra one pound in their wage packet. Not much you might think but the weekly rate at that time was six pounds, twelve shillings a week.

On the subject of gratuities, the first two years at Christmas everyone received a large cake from Canada. The cake was shaped like a doughnut and must have weighed about four pounds and was filled with fruit, nuts and all the goodies, much appreciated by all, especially the wives. We had the cake for two, maybe three years, then it was changed to a turkey which we had for another two years. Then came the merger and I suppose the company became too big.

At Kilmarnock, Scotland

The early years of the company in Kilmarnock were beset with industrial relations problems. The hire and

fire policy allied to seasonal employment operated in Toronto was unheard of here and unacceptable to the Ayrshire workforce or even any workforce in the UK. It was quite a few years before the norm of strike and lay-offs was replaced by full-time employment. This was brought about by bringing back in-house work which had been sub-contracted out, such as front loader, buckets, various attachments to tractors, and farm implements and accessories. My first few months of employment with Massey-Harris were spent in the welding department as charge hand on the main frames for M-H 726 combines. While in this job I was approached by an engineer from the Experimental Department asking if I would like to join the department as he was sure I would find it much more interesting work than what I was doing where I was. Thus commenced my thirty-five years in the Experimental, Development and Test, and finally Engineering as the department has been known through the years. The job as sold to me was certainly interesting and varied and I never regretted a moment of my move.

M-H 744 and 745 Tractors

My experience of Massey-Harris 744 and 745 tractors is rather limited but the decline of the mark was as far as I can remember due to changing from the cast iron sub-frame to a fabricated welded steel support frame. This was still under test when the department moved to Coventry in 1960. Shortly after this the 745 and the new large Ferguson tractor which was under test at the same time vanished from the scene and development concentrated on the MF 35 and 65 range which later became the MF 100 "Red Giants".

An "Australianised" version of the M-H 744D Tractor. This has Australian style front wheels and air cleaner. Sometimes the rear wheels were also of Australian manufacture and marked "Sunshine".

Combine Harvesters

When I started with Massey-Harris the M-H 726 combine was being produced so when I moved to the Experimental section, the M-H 780 was being developed and tested. The main difference between the 726 and the 780 was the drum width being increased from 24" on the 726 to 32" on the 780. The increased threshing capacity created the opportunity to stretch the cutting width of the table from 8 ft to 10 ft and ultimately to 12 ft. If there is such a thing as a happy farmer surely the increasing capacity went some way towards that. One of the headaches at that time was the variety of engines and fuels which, if not available in production machines were submitted for test by the various manufacturers, Austin, Chrysler, Morris, Petter, Lister, Wisconsin and powered by petrol, TVO and diesel.

Around the same time as increasing capacity of the M-H 780, development was going on on smaller combines, namely the M-H 735 and the M-H 750. The 750 was a tractor drawn trailer type machine reputed to produce the best grain sample of any combine, probably because the cutting table and threshing mechanism was the same width. However it was not a great success. Lack of manoeuvrability and bagger type machines were not all that popular. The 735 combine with a 6 ft table was produced for the smaller farmer but again it never reached the sales levels anticipated. The table height control was manual and operated by a hand wheel on the right of the operator's platform. At the end of a day's combining you had a very tired right arm. One of the workshop fitters who was quite a good amateur cartoonist displayed his creations on packing cases etc. I remember one of a 750 combine driver whose

The M-H 780 Combine. A classic of the original M-H self-propelled combine range.

upper torso was turned 180° to his lower half through continually looking round from the tractor watching the height of the cutter bar and the 735 combine driver standing with his right arm like a gorilla's and his hand almost touching the ground. I forget the comments of the drivers on the sketch, probably unprintable.

The MF 400 and 500 combines were developed and produced at Kilmarnock and I was involved from day one on the development and build and later rig and field testing. The basic design was Canadian with original drawings being sent over from Toronto and the machine was known as the TX3. As the drawings were changed to suit UK materials and parts the title became the KX3. The first machine was built in 1955-56 and by the time it was completed the only harvest left in the country was around Elgin in the north east of Scotland. Little testing was done because of the weather but enough was learned to make radical changes for the following year.

The M-H 750 Trailed Combine never caught on and sales were poor. It was a derivative of the highly successful North American made M-H Clipper Combine.

An experimental M-F 400/500 series Combine. Note the right hand access and cab.

Move to Coventry

Around this time rumours began circulating that Experimental was moving to England, to Manchester or Coventry. No one believed it, it just would never happen, how could it. Where could you get parts for spares or build machines? Well it did happen and around thirty percent of the staff were given the opportunity to join the move. About five percent returned to Kilmarnock being unable to settle. Those of us who stayed have few regrets; we settled, brought up families and more or less enjoyed being "sent to Coventry".

As for the merger affecting the company, I suppose they retained the skills and experience especially those of us whose time had been spent mainly on combine harvesters, allied to the fact that Ferguson Engineering had no one with combine experience although they had attempted a TE 20 tractor mounted combine. They also had to pay an increase in wages and salaries as these were much higher than in Kilmarnock. The M-H 745 tractor was discontinued shortly after we came to Coventry. Within three to four years combine design and development was transferred to France thus leaving Coventry Engineering to concentrate solely on tractors.

The Epilogue of MF in the UK

Alas in June of this year, 2002 the remainder of Coventry Engineering was also transferred to France. As I write on this day, Tuesday, 25th June, it has just been announced on radio and television that AGCO is closing the Massey Ferguson Banner Lane Tractor plant at Christmas with a loss of 1,000 jobs. Tractor production will be transferred to France and Brazil.

Evaluating the M-H 735 Combine (Scotland and UK)

Jim Mc Naught

Jim Mc Naught was heavily involved with combine development and had saved some photos of them under evaluation in Scotland.

This page: The M-H 735 Combine under evaluation in Scotland.

James Duncan (President of M-H) and family visiting Scotland's M-H Kilmarnock plant 1951.

On the Heavy Clay Lands (Canada)

Don Mc Vittie

Don Mc Vittie's father was an M-H dealer in Ontario starting in 1938. When his father died suddenly in 1950 Don took over the business. Don's father's first tractor sale had been a green Massey-Harris Pacemaker and he won a prize in 1939 as the dealer selling the most M-H ploughs in Toronto. He had worked with his father in the business since 1946. Don felt little effect of the merger and looked forward to perhaps being able to sell Fergusons. Other dealers he knew at the time had no complaints about the merger. Don remained a dealer until 1959.

There were not many TE and TEA type Fergusons in his part of Ontario at the time, mostly Ford Fergusons. Generally they were considered too small for the heavy clay lands typical of his area. After the merger Don attended various official M-H-F events including a demonstration of the Ferguson side mounted baler at Heathcote. He visited the M-H King Street offices on several occasions, usually in winter time, for service schools, and also went to Detroit for a sales meeting on the introduction of the M-H 50 tractor. At the same time he witnessed M-H 44 tractors being assembled there.

One memorable sale he had was an M-H 26 combine to the late Edward Banting, the nephew of Sir Fred Banting who was the co-discoverer of Insulin. The combine survives to the present day on its original tyres.

In retirement Don is actively involved with the Canadian Massey-Harris and Ferguson enthusiasts, especially through their "Twin-Power Heritage Association Inc." club.

Meanwhile, In Australia ...... (Australia)

(R.V.) Dick Muspratt

Dick Muspratt (R.V.) joined Ferguson in 1947. He established and headed up the local arm of Ferguson in Australia – Harry Ferguson of Australia Ltd. - of which he was the resident Director.

He travelled out with the first consignment of tractors to that country and subsequently chalked up unprecedented sales across the country and in Australasia generally. He recalls that Harry Ferguson himself never made a trip to Australia, but Dick did meet him on two occasions in England when he was invited to tea at the Fergusons' home. Ford Ferguson tractors had previously been sold in Australia. Dick recalls that dealers were dismissive of his wish to train them on the new English Fergusons, claiming that they already knew about them!

Dick travelled Australia widely with James Duncan whenever he was visiting and particularly in relation to the M-H-F acquisition of H. V. McKay Massey-Harris, makers of the Sunshine equipment range. As with the merger of Massey-Harris and Ferguson, many staff were upset.

Dick recalls that these were buoyant days for sales of British manufactured goods into Australia because of preferential "Empire" tariffs. Equally Australia had favoured access for its agricultural products to the British market. These favourable trade arrangements

Hard life in the southern hemisphere! Dick Muspratt in New Britain in October 1950 on the Bismarck Archipelago.

Ploughing on one of the offshore islands.

Demonstrations of three furrow ploughing with a TE 20 between the Gum trees.

Above: A typical demonstration show at a dealer's yard in Australia. Note the Hay Loader and what appears to possibly be a Ferguson Industrial Tractor to the left.

Right: Ferguson TE 20 with Disc Plough in 1949, Dick at the wheel on what appears to have been a cold day somewhere down in Australia.

were all to end when the U.K. later joined the EEC. Dick recalls with more than a hint of sadness how Australia then filled up with manufactured products from the rest of Europe.

Following the merger of Ferguson and Massey-Harris, and subsequent acquisition of H. V. McKay, Sunshine and Ferguson did in effect become sister companies. Ferguson staff were re-located to a Queens Road premises adjacent to the Sunshine administration office. In 1956 Dick became the Assistant to the manager of the new Massey-Harris Sunshine organisation in addition to his duties at Ferguson. Tom Ritchie, a Canadian, was the first Managing Director of the new organisation.

Dick recalls that McKay had been the only farm machinery company to produce farm equipment in the war because steel was required for the war effort. S. S. McKay had lived in the U.K. during the war, arranging shipments of Sunshine machinery into the U.K. A feature of the McKay company when it was taken over was that the staff were quite old with an

A fine line-up of Ferguson TE tractors in a dealership in Sydney 1949.

Above: A quick demonstration of wheel changing with the Ferguson Jack.

average age he thinks of about 55. Also, the company did not have a normal distributor or agency sales and marketing system, but rather a depot system. This proved difficult to merge into the new Massey-Harris-Ferguson company. Similarly there were problems with Ferguson and Massey-Harris dealers – M-H-F had to pay considerable sums out to rationalise them after the mergers. M-H-F could not afford to buy out two larger dealers (Messrs. Crosby and Turner who operated in Melbourne and Sydney, one as British Farm Equipment) and they had to be given

Flying the Australian flag with a Ferguson.

Three tractor generations after the Ferguson TE tractors, here Dick is seen in the M-F Sunshine factory in the 1980s aboard an MF 240 tractor.

extended franchises as compensation. Many of the Ferguson dealers were based on Standard car dealers – remember that Standard made cars as well as the Ferguson tractors.

One of the highlights of his career in Australia was presenting a new TE Ferguson to the Australian Olympic committee – the 50,000th made at Coventry.

Dick also travelled through the USA en route for UK or Australia stopping off in Ferguson's Detroit plant where he became familiar with the TO tractors.

He returned to U.K. in 1960 to undertake various roles with MF. In 1985 he made a visit back to the MF tractor assembly plant in connection with MF 200 series tractors.

Sydney 1957. Dick (left) with Eric Young, Vice-President and Managing Director of the Eastern Hemisphere Division of M-H-F.

Dick hosts another visiting dignitary – Viscount Brookeborough.

An official visit to the Ferguson premises in Melbourne. Three furrow Ferguson Plough inspection for Viscount Brookeborough centre, Dick to left in light suit; C. N. Appleton an M-H-F corporate officer from Toronto to right.

Hosting the boss and his wife in Brisbane. Dick with James Duncan (President of M-H-F) and Mrs Duncan.

Concord West, near Sydney, New South Wales

Duplicate parts department, Sunshine

Right: Geebung, near Brisbane, Queensland
Bottom right: Adelaide, South Australia
Bottom: Perth, Western Australia

Engine Testing (UK)

Nibby Newbold

Nibby Newbold joined the Harry Ferguson Engineering Workshop at Fletchamstead in 1950 as a tractor fitter working under Alex Patterson (see next contribution). Initially he had to get to know about the transmissions and hydraulics but then moved on to the secret large tractor (LTX) development project and did much of the engine testing for this working with the engine designer Alex Senkowski. He recalls that six four cylinder engines were made; four were diesel with in line CAV pumps and the other two were petrol. He also tested the only two cylinder version of this engine ever made. The engine was made at Fletchamstead at Harry Ferguson's other and

newer research facility at Baginton (which he carried on after his departure from M-H-F). The reasons for this testing at Baginton are not clear – perhaps there were more modern facilities there. Nibby recalled that there was talk of the two cylinder engine being used in Massey-Harris Pony tractors in France, and possibly also in some application for Japan.

Nibby fondly recalls the Standard 23 C diesel engine which was fitted to the Ferguson 35s as the "Vanguard" engine since the same basic engine was used in Standard Vanguard cars, and the endeavours to make the diesel version better starting with a Ricardo cylinder head. He also tested the Lamp Oil engines

Nibby Newbold (rear) in the service workshop at Banner Lane, Coventry with overseas guests. Tractors on which dealers could not resolve problems were brought back here for rectification.

that were fitted to Ferguson tractors for certain export markets describing them as of low power and having to be started on petrol like the more common TVO engines. On occasions he would take Lamp oil and TVO tractors to Harry Ferguson's estate where the "boss" would evaluate them.

When the Fletchamstead facility (100,000 sq. ft.) was closed in about 1954-1955, engineering with engine testing moved to the No. 3 workshop at Banner Lane where he tested the Perkins P3 and P6 type engines. Ironically Harry Ferguson had used this same workshop in 1945 for about 6-9 months prior to establishing the Fletchamstead facility. A P6 engine was fitted into an MF 65 tractor twith three turbos. This tractor was made up for the field demonstrators who, he said, "wanted to mess about!" Whilst at Banner Lane he was much involved with the testing of hydraulic pumps.

Nibby does have a claim to fame as regards the preparation of the tractors that went on the South Pole expedition with Sir Edmund Hillary. He reversed the fans to pull heat into the radiator from the engine. Otherwise he says, there were relatively few modifications made to the basic tractors besides electrical and fitting of tracks and reduction gearboxes.

Later the M-F engineering workshop facility was moved again, this time to Maudslay Road.

And Nibby's main memory of the consequences of the merger – loss of the free Ferguson Christmas party with drinks and all!

Top: Nibby preparing a Ferguson 35 for a dynamometer test at Harry Ferguson's engineering facility on Fletchamstead Highway, Coventry.

Centre: The Dynamometer control panel at Fletchamstead Highway.

Bottom: One of the four cylinder engines for the Ferguson LTX tractors on test at Fletchamstead Highway.

A Wealth of Information (N Ireland and UK)

Alex Patterson

Massey-Harris-Ferguson, Coventry.

The "Fletch" as Ferguson's Fletchamstead research and development engineering facility was called where Alex Patterson had some 500 men under him. This shot is taken after the merger – the Ferguson sign has been replaced by Massey-Harris-Ferguson.

Alex Patterson was Harry Ferguson's Engineering Superintendent in charge of about 500 men at Ferguson's Fletchamstead research and development engineering facility. This facility was of course of major significance to Massey-Harris at the merger because it gave them access to Ferguson's high engineering standards. The extent of these facilities was illustrated in a series of photos which comprised an educational film strip titled "Lab Testing". Unfortunately there were no accompanying captions, but many are self-explanatory.

Alex started with Harry Ferguson in 1938 in Belfast, Northern Ireland when he was 17. He served with Ferguson, then Massey-Harris-Ferguson and finally Massey-Ferguson until 1967. I was privileged to talk to him over a long lunch at a pub near his home in Kenilworth in April 2002, and subsequently visit again and talk on the telephone. Alex has a wealth of information about Ferguson, M-H-F and MF days sufficient for an encyclopaedia. I wanted to meet him to clarify a few points about M-H-F era. I had the points listed – it was the only way to focus on the period otherwise lunch would have gone through to tea, supper and breakfast the next day! But with his Irish charm a lot more than the points I clarify here came across and it was a perfect "Ferguson" balance

to the lunch I had had two years previously with Len Boon on the "Massey" side. Both, despite their advancing years, have incredible powers of recall and a perennial love of the Massey and Ferguson eras in which they worked. They enlightened me about the nature of this great period in agricultural machinery history.

Alex was back home in Ireland at the time the merger was announced having heard nothing of the on-going negotiations. He was greeted at the airport on arrival home to be told (jokingly) by a colleague that he had "lost his job".

In his role as Engineering Superintendent he often had to work behind locked doors admitting no one other than on the orders of Harry Ferguson!

The Merger and the Nature of the Two Companies

Initially Alex thought there could be good in the agreement in that it would give Ferguson access to Massey-Harris castings. They turned out not to be as good as he thought. On a visit to M-H in Toronto he found the plant there old-fashioned. He made a summary comparison of engineering in the two camps as "Ferguson engineers" and "Massey-Harris blacksmiths". Both companies had managements which could be improved at the time. Farmers may

ENGINEERING SCHEME NUMBERS.   NOVEMBER, 1954.

ES.		ES.	
1.	Tractor TEA.20 Mods.	82.	Mid-Mounted Mower.
2.	Tractor Exp. Development.	83.	L.O.Development
3.	Box - Transport Mods.	85.	Furrow Width Adjuster Dev.
4.	Cultivator - 9-KE-Mods.	87.	3-Furrow 8" Plough Dev.
5.	Cultivator - 9-SKE Mods.	88.	30 cwt. Trailer.
7.	Harrow - Spike Tooth Mods.	91	Automatic Potato Planter.
8.	Harrow - Spring Tooth Mods.	92.	Fert.Attach. for Grain Drill.
9.	Mower 5' - Mods.	93.	Two-Way Plough Development.
10.	Plough 10" 2-Furrow Mods.	95.	Seeding Attachment for Tiller.
11.	Plough 10" 3-Furrow Mods.	96.	Trailer Hitch Development.
12.	Plough 12" 2-Furrow Mods.	98.	Hammermill.
13.	Plough 12" 3-Furrow Mods.	99.	Mark II Spreader Dev.
14.	Plough 16" 1-Furrow Mod.	100	Diesel Tractor Development.
15.	Ridger Mods.	101.	Post Hole Digger Mods.
16.	Saw Mods.	102	Offset Disc Harrow.
17.	Scoop - Earth Mods.	104	Side Delivery Rake (American).
19.	Tiller.	106	Partridge Scarer.
20.	Trailer.	107.	Universal Marker.
21.	Tractor Maintenance.	108.	Trailer Moving Bed Assy.
22.	Implement Maintenance.	110	Hesford Winch Development.
24.	Potato Planter.	111.	Mounted Disc Harrow.
25.	General Supplies.	112.	Corn and Cotton Planter.
26.	Weeder.	113.	2-Furrow Rev.Plough.
27.	Sub Soiler.	114.	Large Wheel Spreader dev.
29.	Grain Drill.	115.	5-ton Trailer Development.
30.	Seeder Unit.	116.	85m/m Petrol Engine Dev.
31.	Hay Sweep.	117.	2-Way Soil Scoop.
32.	Hay Rake.	118.	Mounted Spring Tooth Harrow.Dev.
33.	Manure Loader.	119.	Work for H.Ferguson Research.
34.	Manure Spreader.	120.	Stress and Strain Dev.
35.	Jack - Tractor.	121.	Potato Planter Mods.
36.	Pulley - P.T.O.	122.	Steerage Hoe Mods.
37.	General Shop Work.	123.	French Spike Tooth Harrow.
38.	Plant Machinery.	124.	Extra Narrow Tractor.
40.	Purchase of imps, other than Ferguson.	127.	Single Arm Coulter Dev.
41.	Work for Mr.Ferguson or new equipment.	130.	Disc Tiller.
		131.	Epicyclic Gear Prod.Tractor.
43.	Harrow - Disc - Development.	132.	Mounted Sweeper.
46.	Woodsaw Development.	133.	Elevating Stationery Hammermill.
47.	Beet Lifter.	135.	Mounted P.T.O.Unit.
48.	Pest Control Spray.	137.	Silage Harvester.
49.	Tyre Girdles.	138.	Hedgecutter.
50.	Diff. Steerage Hoe.	139.	Subsoiler, Mark II.
52.	Disc Plough.	140.	Ripping Saw.
53.	Swath Turner.	141.	Exp. Bar Point Base.
54.	Repro. of Tractor Drawings.	142.	3-ton Trailer Development.
55.	Steerage Hoe Development.	143.	Self-Sealing Coupling.
57.	Stabilizer.	144.	Ferguson Multi-Purpose Blade and Scarifier Kit.
58.	General Office Work.		
59.	14" Plough.	145.	Quick Release Coupling.
60.	L-TE-60 Tractor.	146.	Trailer Hitch for L-TX-Tractor.
61	Industrial Tractor.	147.	Jointer Blade Development.
62.	General Implement Work.	148.	Diesel Narrow Tractor.
63.	Production Manure Loader Dev.	149.	Shorrock (Superchargers) Ltd.
64.	Cantilever Loader Type Dev.	150.	Irrigation Pump.
65.	Manure Spreader Attach. Dev.	151.	Vineyard Ploughs.
66.	Rotary Hoe Development.	154.	Middlebuster.
67.	Con. of Non-Ferguson Imps.	155.	Position Control for Tractor.
69.	Swinging Drawbar.	156.	Power Take-Off Manure Spreader.
70.	V.O.Tractor Development.	157.	Seeding Attach - Disc Tiller.
72.	3-Furrow Disc Plough.	158.	Buck Rake.
73.	Test House, Test Ground Equip.	159.	2-Furrow 16" Plough.
74.	Blade Terracer.	162.	13 Spring Tine Tiller.
76.	Front Wheel Weights.	163.	High Lift Loader - Large.
77.	Potato Spinner Mods.	164.	90m/m V.O.Engine.
78.	Drawing Office Supplies.	166.	Side Del. Rake & Swathturner.
		167.	4-Furrow 10" Plough Dev.

Alex Patterson had a very wide range of projects on at Fletchamstead in 1954.

have liked Massey-Harris sales style more because they were more old-fashioned in their approach whereas Ferguson had adopted more of a car sales approach which was perhaps less attractive to naturally conservative farmers.

Involvement with Other Sections and Projects of M-H-F

It should be remembered that Alex worked for the Ferguson research facility and not on the production of Ferguson tractors by the Standard Motor Co. In the merger period he stayed in this role. However the research facility never became involved with the development of the latter day Massey-Harris 333, 444 and 555 tractors at Racine in Wisconsin, USA. In fact Alex never visited there or the Ferguson Inc. plant at Detroit. However French Massey-Harris did get some of his attention by way of the development of a new Pony tractor. Alex was dubious as to the need for this given that by this time narrow and vineyard Ferguson tractors were available. In the event a prototype was made with (as far as he can recall) the Ferguson System incorporated, but this project never went any further. The tractor was about 20 hp and used a Senkowski designed two cylinder diesel engine which had been developed along with the four cylinder engine for the LTX tractor, and a six cylinder engine for an eventual large Ferguson tractor. The engines all had the same bore. The two cylinder engine never came into production.

Regarding the M-H-F acquisition of Sunshine in Australia, Alex and colleagues were not involved. But

it was not regarded as an advanced manufacturing facility, more an expansion opportunity. Similarly the Coventry end of M-H-F had no knowledge of the Massey-Harris Pitt tractor project or the Massey-Harris prototype 75 tractor.

To my surprise, Alex and his team were never used to "improve" on Massey-Harris tractor hydraulics of the day. The only involvement with a production Massey-Harris tractor seems to have been testing of a 745 tractor. A test bed rig was made to sort out front axle and chassis problems.

The Side-Mounted Combines

Although it has been reported that there was a single right-hand mounted combine in the batch of prototypes produced, Alex is adamant there was no such machine and that unfortunately the original photograph has become reversed. This is not an uncommon happening and to this day AGCO have such a photo of a tractor ploughing hanging on their walls at Coventry! Alex knew nothing of the French Ferguson combine – I was quite pleased to have pulled this piece of Ferguson history across him! When I showed him the design he was horrified at the way the Ferguson tractor had been sliced into three pieces to accommodate the combine. Alex was never enamoured with the side mounted Ferguson combine project. As he pointed out - a farmer could have bought a good used Massey-Harris combine – a market leader – for less money than a Ferguson side mounted.

He confirmed that the combines could be detached

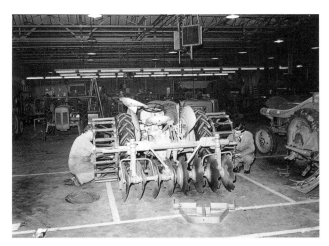

Working on Ferguson Tractor with a set of Ferguson Heavy Duty Disc Harrows and cage wheels for use in rice paddy fields. Special "rice fields" were made at the Training Centre for evaluating these machines in the UK.

None of the original Ferguson Side-mounted Combines survive. Something had to be done! Over ten years ago John Moffitt had one recreated and showed it at the Royal Agricultural Show held annually at Stoneleigh just a few miles from Fletchamstead where the originals were made.

from the tractor quite quickly and the tractor could be left with the axle extension in place for normal work. This would save on detachment time.

The U.K. had no involvement in the side-mounted balers and foragers made in the USA.

What made the LTX tractor so good?

Quite simple, says Alex. All the experience of Ford Ferguson and Ferguson tractors had gone into the design of the machine.

A mock-up of the LTX Tractor modelled as the Ferguson 60 at Ferguson's Fletchamstead workshops.

There was much consideration of torque and flywheel characteristics and a new hydraulic pump with three square pistons that worked at up to 6000 psi. Additionally there was only a single main hydraulic lever for routine use like the old TE 20 in UK and TO 20 and TO 30 tractors out of Detroit. A second, smaller hydraulic lever was however provided. This was a "sensitivity" control which would be set once and for all for each task depending on the type of work, e.g. light rowcrop or heavy draft. This smaller lever controlled an internal link back to the control valve on the hydraulic pump.

Sadly the North American side of M-H-F were un-persuadable about the superior performance of the LTX. I asked if the design of the TO 35 and the LTX could have been merged but Alex was certain that they could not. He simply thinks that the TO 35 should never have been!

Alex recalls that one LTX tractor was sent to the USA for demonstration and evaluation, but was never returned and presumably scrapped.

Involvement with the Ferguson 35 Tractor Design

Alex's team had no involvement with the design of the TO 35 tractor in America. This had been solely the project of Ferguson Inc.'s chief engineer Herbert Klemm in Detroit, USA. Alex says, with a smile, that his only involvement was to criticise it! He never liked the two lever hydraulic concept of the tractor, and of course it ended up with an inferior engine to the cancelled British designed LTX tractor. The two lever hydraulics for regular use were deemed too complex and difficult to understand for the average operator – particularly in third world situations.

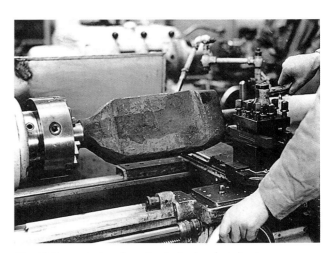

Alex Patterson's hand on the lathe turning down a crankshaft for a two cylinder engine for an LTX type Tractor.

I have puzzled over the fact that Harry Ferguson had a tractor design on each side of the Atlantic going in separate directions – the TO 35 and LTX. "Why?" I asked Alex. "Was it to see who could come up with the best design – setting one team against the other?" "Possibly," replied Alex philosophically!

MF 65 Development in the UK

Although of M-H-F North America design, there were frantic activities at the start of production of this tractor in the U.K with Alex having much concern for the quality of the front axle which he had to rectify almost as it was coming off the production line. He was not over complimentary on the quality of the first tractors! Slight tin-work modification was also made to the American design.

M-F 65 Tractor manufacture at Banner Lane.

Below: Alex Patterson (left) with technician Alan Starley (centre, and see page 173) at a 21st birthday party for the Ferguson TE 20 tractor.

Nigel Liney (see also page 123) demonstrating an early MF 65 Tractor at Stoneleigh.

The Prototype Sugar Beet Harvester

Alex explained that it had been a well-established Ferguson philosophy that when a new implement was under consideration then the market leader of the day should be fully analysed and evaluated. From this procedure would be established a basic design which had to be improved upon. In the case of the sugar beet harvester this was not done. End of story – abandonment of an unsuccessful machine!

Why the Ferguson Reluctance to Adopt Perkins Engines?

Harry Ferguson instinctively did not like diesel engines. Good though the performance of Perkins

A completely unrestricted view is obtained when using a reversible tractor in reverse.

engines was, their propensity to oil leakage offended the Ferguson engineering establishment! Ferguson did in fact help with the resolution of some of these problems and the Perkins P3 engine had to be fitted to TE 20 tractors for export to Yugoslavia. But this was in M-H-F days after Harry Ferguson had departed from the scene! Eventually courses were held at the M-H-F Stoneleigh Training Centre for the large number of P3 engines that were being retro fitted by British farmers. M-H-F of course had Perkins engines in their combines and the M-H 744 and 745 tractors. The P6 engine had been thought of for the LTX tractor but Harry Ferguson was greatly offended by the oil leaks despite it producing the 45 hp needed for the LTX! Reg Ayers of Perkins made repeated and persistent attempts to get Harry Ferguson to adopt the P3 engines for the TE 20 but it was a case of seed sown on stony ground!

The Reversible Tractor Conceived by Durham University

Alex was well aware of this project but believes it was a flawed concept other than for loader use. The fundamental flaw was that rear steering for rowcrop work is very insensitive for rapid course correction. Think about it and realise how right he is!

Left: Working example of the Reversible Ferguson Tractor conceived by the University of Durham.

Below: The Reversible Ferguson Tractor seen fitted with front mounted hoe and vertical hydraulic lift at rear.

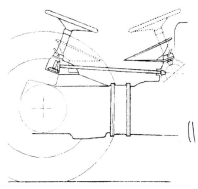

Starting M-H-F Industrials

M-H-F's first major move into production of industrial equipment came with the acquisition of Mid Western Equipment which manufactured Davis equipment. Alex knew Charlie Davis. JCB had nearly bought him out before M-H-F – but Albert Thornbrough obviously got in to gear quickly. After the acquisition a major conference was held in Coventry attended by some 60 people. Davis was not impressed by the tortuous proceedings! – but by then he had sold out.

Lamp Oil Tractors

Engines adapted to use lamp oil – low quality paraffin, were made primarily for the Turkish and Greek markets where only low grade paraffin was available. Normal TVO engines used paraffin of about 50 octane rating, but lamp oil engines used 25-4 octane fuel by having the compression ratio reduced to 4.5:1. This reduced the power rating to a maximum of 22.9 belt hp compared to the about 25 hp of TVO engines.

Finally – the Grey and Gold

A meeting of 30-40 people was held to decide upon the colour for the British Ferguson 35 tractor. Sales and marketing were in the mood for pastel shades like pink and beige. Alex was not impressed. As the delegates went for lunch, Alex engaged in conversation with a paint salesman who had some copper coloured paint. A tractor chassis was sprayed in the lunch hour and placed in the distance. After lunch it was spotted by management and somewhat admired and, on closer inspection, was accepted. The paint soon turned green! To counteract this the copper in the paint was replaced with aluminium but, according to Alex, it was never quite as bright and smart as the original.

Above left: The Reversible Ferguson Tractor seen fitted with a Shawnee Loader.

Above right: Detail of the steering arrangement. A small slave steering box is linked to the main steering box by a shaft. The steering box and column can be spigoted to either steering box and held by clamp. The seat has the same spigot and clamp.

Below: The M-F Director of UK Engineering (right) presenting a television set as a leaving present to Alex Patterson.

Alex was responsible for arranging the launch of the FE 35 to dealers in the UK. This was at the Leofric Hotel in Coventry and involved him in assembling an 8-10 ft. high stand in the ballroom on which the tractor was placed. All sheet metal was removed from the tractor until immediately before the event in order that no one could have a sneak preview!

"Service Pays All Ways" (England, Eire, Scotland, Wales, Italy, India)

Bill Percival

I joined Harry Ferguson Ltd. on August 14th, 1947. My practical knowledge of crops and cultivations was virtually non-existent and impeded my ability to talk with any authority to farmers and dealers. However, Peter Delingpole, the Chief Demonstrator soon taught me a great deal as we travelled around the country attending shows and demonstrations. There were some enlightening experiences on these demonstrations, and in my later service role! Here are a few:

Comedy in Ireland

The dealership in Athenry in Galway was nowhere to be found on arrival. An employee took me to the workshop down a very narrow passage. There was no semblance of any major piece of Ferguson equipment, but it was well stocked with coffins! I could do nothing to prepare a demonstration until I met the dealer. A message came that he would meet me after dinner. I waited till 11 pm. Apparently he turned up at my hotel after midnight where he stayed drinking into the small hours. I eventually caught up with him on Sunday afternoon by which time a couple of loads of equipment had arrived from the Dublin distributorship. I had spent the morning watching churchgoers arrive in horses and carts, often disgorging themselves of the previous night's intake on the roadside. On the next day prior to the demonstration a part broke and we had to raise a blacksmith at 10 am to effect a repair. The demonstration went surprisingly well, but I told the dealer that his standards were not those expected of a Ferguson dealer. He told me not to worry – it would be taken care of. Less than a year later his premises were burnt down.

Scottish Hillsides

After the Irish trip I was detailed to go up to Scotland demonstrating hillside ploughing. This was a new concept for the Ferguson System and I had never done it before. I was only given theoretical instruction before departing as there was no suitable land near Coventry. Some of the most difficult terrain that it was possible to find had been selected in order to prove that the operation

was possible or not. To put it mildly, I was scared when I started to plough. No safety frame in those days and there had been fatal accidents on such sites. The demonstration was not a success.

A Row with Mr Ferguson

A demonstration in Evesham proved to have the most influence on my career with Harry Ferguson Ltd.

It was a large event on behalf of the local dealer. About 500 farmers turned up. There was a possibility that Mr Ferguson and his family would come and knowing that he was a perfectionist, I did my best

Still not united! An Irish Massey-Harris and Ferguson Year Book of 1955.

Now a rare tractor – the Lamp Oil Version of the Ferguson Tractor.

to make sure everything was well prepared and that the programme would go smoothly. Most of our equipment was to be demonstrated by my four demonstrators. Everything was going quite well about an hour into the demonstration – at least most of the farmers thought so. Then along came Mr Ferguson plus wife and family, plus a number of directors from the Ferguson company in Detroit. Immediately he started to criticise everything. Even the farmers got annoyed with him and called to him to leave us alone. Each time he watched an implement operating he would get hold of me and give me a dressing down. The final straw came when we were to demonstrate the steerage hoe for the first time in public. We had had no practical instruction in its use and were really working by trial and error and not making too bad a job - and the farmers seemed satisfied. Mr Ferguson walked over to me very purposefully and started giving instructions that the steerage hoe was to be returned to Coventry with the present settings. I could stand no more, so grabbed hold of his arm, started to shake it and told him he had ruined the whole demonstration and that I was not prepared to stand for any more abuse from him. He thereupon left in his Rolls Royce. I was convinced that my reign with the Ferguson company was over and decided to return to my home in Devon where I stayed for 12 days. What really annoyed me was that on returning to Coventry no one seemed to have noticed my absence. I think it was then that I decided my future was with MF. I was eventually summoned to meet Trevor Knox the Sales Manger who had been with Harry Ferguson since he left school. I told him that the stupid old

so-and-so had ruined the demonstration! Though I did survive, I was in future largely kept out of Mr Ferguson's way!

Claridges Hotel

I almost bumped into Mr Ferguson again at Claridges Hotel in London on the occasion of a big gathering of dignitaries and press. Ferguson had an office on the first floor of a block opposite the hotel with a tractor displayed in a small reception area. I had to help partly dismantle the tractor and convey it in a small passenger lift down to the ground floor and across to the hotel in assembled state. It was there that Mr Ferguson made his historic drive down the steps of Claridges Hotel and into the ballroom. This was very widely reported.

Service Representative

Soon I was offered the job of Service Representative covering the south-west of England, much of Wales and including the Scillies and Channel Islands. The objective was to call on dealers every three weeks. It was hard work and not good for family life. We had to cajole, persuade and often threaten dealers into achieving better performances. They could be difficult as we were asking them to spend money to achieve a style and standard of service never before achieved in the trade We wanted a regular monthly visit to every tractor they had sold, inside or outside of the warranty period. Ferguson was a pioneer in this style of servicing – the farmer only paid when work was required and for parts. Probably the most difficult dealer to comply with our Ferguson system was a dealer in Wales. Without doubt a chronic alcoholic. Whatever time of day I called on him I would find him in the pub. He was none too amenable to installing the Ferguson Service System. Probably the worst time to call was Cheltenham Festival week in March/April. All the dealers drinking and horsey pals from miles around would assemble in the pub prior to going to Cheltenham and few left before being "many points in the wind".

Italian Neurotic and Lamp Oil Tractors

For almost seven weeks I was stuck with a non-smoking, non-drinking Italian neurotic in 1950. Additionally he was a terrible driver and his main drink seemed to be bicarbonate of soda for his ulcers. I had been sent out to Milan to deal with problems they were having with their lamp oil tractors. This was a new model which Ferguson had developed for places such as Italy. There were only limited numbers of these tractors produced, but they were nevertheless important. The neurotic had a routine of being on the road at 6 am and going to bed at 9.30 pm. One night in Turin I stayed up later on my own, consuming brandies. At 11.30 pm the barman asked if I needed a young lady. I didn't, went to bed, but was awakened at 4 am with the lady who had just returned from a cabaret club hanging over my bed quoting 50 USD or £30! – probably £100 in present day money. I got rid of her and woke a few hours later with a big headache!

A note on the Lamp Oil tractors

They were specifically designed to operate in countries where olive oil was an important crop and Italy as, I believe, one of the main customers for this type of tractor. As for the problems involved, from my recollections (it is over 50 years ago!) the main one was excessive engine wear due to poor air cleaner maintenance in a very dusty environment in the conditions prevailing during the normal hot summers experienced, particularly in southern Italy. Although hard to put over to customers, it was often necessary to change the oil in the air cleaner twice a day due to the formation of mud in the oil bath. Failure to do this resulted in abrasive air being carried into the engine with excessive wear the result.

The Merger

The merger did lead to a good deal of friction between the Ferguson and M-H factions. Each company felt that the managers should take the top jobs, Massey because they had bought Ferguson, Ferguson because they had the best and more efficient organisation. We in Ferguson felt we had been sold out without any guarantees of employment or position. There was a great deal of lobbying for jobs right the way through the organisation from the top to the bottom. From being a nice friendly family concern, Ferguson and I suppose Massey to some extent were being turned into a rather bitter company where "dog eat dog" was the order of the day. My department, Service, had to rationalise like the others. Maxie Henderson became UK service manger and Charles Voss took over Export. We carried on as normal with the Massey side attending courses at Stoneleigh and the Ferguson people attending schools in France, Germany and Kilmarnock. Later, after M-H-F acquired Perkins, we all went on courses at Peterborough.

More unrest followed when Al Thornbrough took

Above: An M-F Overseas Service Training Conference. Bill organised these with Charles Voss (see also page 184).

Opposite: Delegates of an M-F Service Training Conference held at the M-F Training Centre in Stoneleigh; Charles Voss in the middle front row.

over from James Duncan. Management consultants McKinsey were appointed. M-H-F were the first to employ such people in the UK. We felt harassed and were never certain whether at the end of the day we would have a job.

Promoting Service – SERVICE PAYS ALL WAYS

After the merger Charles Voss and I held a world-wide Export Service Manager's Conference in the U.K. to further generate the ideals promoted by Harry Ferguson. The week long event was a tremendous success and a book covering all aspects of the conference was produced, a copy of which I still keep for my own records. Towards the end of the fifties I went on a twenty country world-wide trip promoting service as a follow up to the conference. It was a terrific job. The first stop was India where the boss Hari Nanda of our distributors Escort asked serious questions about the commitment of M-H-F. The next morning I realised he had taped my answers using a microphone inside a rose in his buttonhole. It turned

out to be not too sinister as Hari had just taken up the distributorship for a range of micro-equipment and was testing it out! But more sinister manoeuvres did occur. In Holland the main distributor got the Ferguson man very drunk and took him to a night club and found him an escort girl, hid a movie camera in his bedroom and recorded the antics. Although nothing became of it, the lesson was all too obvious.

Improvisation in India (India)

David Perrott

I was with Harry Ferguson, India in Bangalore as the service Manager at the time of the merger with Massey-Harris. As there was a Massey-Harris service manager (Hadrian Cheesman), I took over specialised new implement development for Indian conditions, having seen many attempts at this in the territory we covered. The territory was India which included Pakistan in those days! Previously I had spent more than 50% of my time travelling and been involved with heavy correspondence – chiefly concerning warranty details and with central government.

It was common to sow different seed at the same time. Some were sown shallow to germinate quickly whilst the soil was still moist, others were sown more deeply. This was also an insurance in case one crop failed, and further one crop might provide protection for the other. I had seen six men walking behind a tiller, hand-feeding seeds into funnels feeding down tubes behind each tine. I developed a drill which had several adjustable compartments and with adjustable openings for the seed. Seed was kept flowing by revolving rubber discs. It was crude but cheap!

Another major problem was cultivating rice paddy fields. I developed cage wheels which were slightly smaller diameter than the tractor tyres so that they did not constantly have to be removed and refitted. By trial and error we had to reduce the number of cross braces so that the mud would fall out of the cages and not accumulate. To prevent the front of the tractor lifting and turning over with cage wheels fitted, and also to create the correct mud texture for hand transplanting of the young rice plants, I attached the front gang from a set of disc harrows. This "sliced" the soil, so then we fitted two following adjustable boards behind the discs to help bring the soil together again, and also support the weight of the discs. This in turn provided thrust to the top link operating the Ferguson depth control. The cage wheels thereby

A demonstration for cage wheels for at the School of Farm Mechanisation after David Perrot's idea had been accepted.

Introducing and demonstrating the Ferguson 35 in India.

Planting rice at Stoneleigh.

provided traction and at the same time produced the necessary puddling of the soil – or mud as it really was. I'm pleased top say that the "Paddy Wheels" went straight into production from my drawings (after being signed off by an engineer!) and were used in a number of territories. The disc and board implement was to evolve as the Ferguson "Paddy Disc Harrow".

It is perhaps amusing to recall an Indian home bred piece of improvisation. In 1950-1954 when I was there, the TE 20 TVO model had a very low compression ratio. I actually saw replacement pistons being cast at the side of the road and turned down on a hand operated bow string lathe!

I also saw governor weights being cast. When an engine was serviced the pivots were never replaced until the weights came through the timing cover! The extensive resulting damage could still be patched up – time did not matter. It was all a fascinating experience in India.

Ralph Haynes, a Coventry Engineer took over my development work for some years after I left India in 1954.

Demonstration of a tracked MF Rice Combine. M-H pioneered the use of tracks on their first mass produced Self-propelled Combine, the M-H 21.

The world rice crop was taken very seriously by M-F. They had a specially designed rice cultivation area at the Stoneleigh School of Farm Mechanisation and actually held a rice conference there in 1966. Here rice sowing is demonstrated.

Fergusons Sold and Remembered; and Ferguson stories! (Belgium, Germany, France)

Maurice Pol-Fraikin (translated from Maurice's original French script)

My father was a well-known specialist in threshing machines. He also had a small workshop selling and repairing agricultural implements.

Health problems and the war deprived me of higher education (I did not like it much, it is true). In 1946, having done army service for a few months, I rejoined the family business as an apprentice. Since the end of the war, contrary to the other neighbouring countries, the Belgian tractor market opened up without importation restrictions because we did not have local manufacturers. So my father received two Farmall tractors (type A and H). The machines did not please customers too much. The best selling tractors of the period were the Fordson Major and previously, the row-crop John Deeres. But we could not sell these marques, not being their agent ...

The name FERGUSON (associated with FORD = Ford Ferguson) reached me via an uncle. Uncle Edouard had seen these little grey tractors in Reims where they were being sold by M. Mogen. The latter had praised the merits of these extraordinary little machines and he had advised Edouard to tell us to write to Ford-France to ask for the agency of this marque. We consequently wrote to Ford-France in this way. A reply arrived several months later explaining that the Ford/Ferguson agreements were broken and that manufacture under the "Ferguson" name was

Field Marshall Montgomery in the company of Sir John Black visiting his Coventry factory where the Fergusons were made. (from the files of Maurice Pol-Fraikin).

in preparation in Britain. In the spring of 1946, a Richard Waller calling himself a Ferguson representative announced his visit. Actually Mr Waller came to announce that the Ferguson equipment would be sold in Belgium by the "Société Imperia" which also was to sell Standard-Vanguard and Triumph cars. Mr Waller, who was American, was quick in business. Hardly had a few words been exchanged when he asked my father to get out his chequebook. And that is how a first order of eighteen TE-A 20 tractors was made - the first six tractors due to arrive in September.

But times were difficult because, in the meantime, my father had been injured in an accident caused by a US army lorry. It fell to me therefore to carry on, with difficulty, the management of our small business.

One day, Richard Waller returned to urge me to take part in a "Ferguson System" training course. It was decided that I would leave for Coventry at the end of August.

I accompanied Robert Vanhoorebeke, an agronomy engineer. Fortunately, this man had a knowledge of English and England (unlike me!). We crossed the Channel – it was my first encounter with the sea...Then, we took the train from Paddington to Leamington-Spa. There we landed at the Manor House Hotel where we stayed for a week or so. The day after our arrival we were taken over by a delegate of Ferguson, Mr. Miloslaw Vapenick, a Czech and ex RAF. The Education Centre was at Kenilworth and included classrooms. The demonstrations on the land were carried out at the military flying ground at Snitterfield. The classes were given by Mr. John Chambers (Harry Ferguson's no.1 assistant) assisted by Mr Denis Purchas. There were 18 students of whom 12 were British, two Spanish, two Dutch and two Belgian. Everything was done in English and this was not easy. There were misunderstandings. For example, Denis Purchas began a statement by saying, "first of all" and I had understood that he was talking about a "festival"! Nevertheless, all went well and the courses were excellent.

Besides this, England appeared to us to be very gloomy. Food there was still rationed. At the hotel we were served powdered eggs. And I remember the day that there was some sort of food poisoning – everybody, even the great Ferguson directors were unable to refrain from emitting "unseemly sounds"!

Since the beginning of the course, Robert and I had understood that there would be a problem with the ploughs and other Ferguson implements. We knew that our Belgian clients would not like them. On the other hand, we were delighted with the tractor itself and since then, everybody knows why. For my part, at 23 years old I was very impressed by Harry Ferguson's theories on the rescue of agriculture and the struggle against hunger in the world. I returned home with a missionary's spirit.

The first six tractors had just arrived. One encouraging fact came into view: I sold the first tractor in Belgium to a farmer by the name of Gailliez at Estinnes-au-Mont. In fact, M. Gailliez had placed his order by telephone. Neither talk nor demonstration were necessary to convince him because he knew of the advantages of the Ferguson system from his family who lived in France.

Since the autumn of 1947 we had begun a tour of demonstrations with Milo Vapenick who, in spite of his attraction for the women of the region, devoted himself to demonstrating one-way ploughing to our Belgian farmers. One-way ploughing was mandatory to Belgian farmers, and with Belgian reversible ploughs of which the Belgian manufacturer Melotte was the champion. Moreover, they did not want discs but "coulters" and "razetters" with a view to burying the manure. This problem would not be resolved until much later, at first by the adaptation of the frames/bodies. They attempted to introduce the American "Lindeman" reversible plough but the mechanism was fragile and the price too high. In 1948, two young mechanics, the Baeke brothers, built an excellent plough carried by return at a "quarter of a turn" which was a success and contributed widely to the success of Ferguson tractors in Belgium.

But confronted with the growing importation of American tractors, Fordson (which were sold 20% cheaper than the Ferguson), David Brown (which had three point linkage) and also the first German diesel tractors, the spread of the Ferguson system was not easy. Problems were the necessity to purchase implements, fuel consumption and the weakness of the traction of the good little grey one.

Selling tractors was always subject to stiff competition from other makes. Here a Ford-Ferguson and Ferguson Tractor take on the big boys.

From 1948 one had seen the appearance of the "vaporiser kits" to convert the petrol engine to TVO. Later, there were the Perkins engine conversions.

The lack of traction for towing two axle trailers was a big problem, especially in the sugar beet areas. Naturally the Ferguson three tons trailer was a great help. But its capacity was only 3 tonnes! The farmers wanted to carry more in a single journey! Everything was tried: dual the rear wheels, winch to pull the heavy trailer out of the fields, steel wheels with lugs. But the most extreme idea was to fit a half-ton bucket supported by four posts above the tractor itself to carry beet. This was found to make the tractor heavier and 500 kilos more could be carried. The engine of the poor little grey withstood the extra load!

In 1950 the 1,000th tractor delivery was made into Belgium. The success was not negligible but it was not always easy to compete with the others. In the meantime Fords had returned with the 8N and 8NAN. There were more and more German marques, all with diesel engines and, often, with the differential lock device. This accessory was not introduced by MF until much later, on the 35X tractor.

It is historically interesting to recall that, in the fifties, the Swiss engineer Willi Salzman built a differential lock device kit which could be fitted to the TE 20 models (from no. 325,001 onwards) and later to the FE 35. Enough is not known as to whether this non-original device facilitated the sale of more Ferguson tractors to compete with the Germans.

For my part, I lived

through all these years with periods of satisfaction and otherwise. At the time of the Ferguson and Massey-Harris merger in 1953 disagreements appeared between the different importers. My father was badly affected and disgusted by certain practices.

At the same time, I had the opportunity to work with the Ferguson importer to the Belgian Congo and I stayed there until 1958.

On account of my eagerness to defend Mr Harry Ferguson's theories some people gave me the nickname of "Ferguson".

Family reasons forced me to return to Europe in the spring of 1958. I did not have work. At the request of several dealers, I undertook the business of supplying accessories for tractors, which Ferguson did not produce, e.g. cabs, seats, hour-meters and also fitting conversion engines, vaporisers, differential lock kits etc etc. This I did with great success until 1991, the date of my retirement. I now live happily and prosperous, thanks to Ferguson! I have not forgotten to keep in my garage a nice "little grey" TEA-20 Serial no. 260499, 1952, which I maintain with love. I saw it in 1987, in the throes of death against a tree in an orchard in Pay de Herve. I had the option of buying another, perfectly reconditioned. But I was moved by the desire to repair one myself. I acquired my beloved TE 20! Apart from the replacement of the water pump and several other details it was principally a matter of removing the rust, de-greasing and cleaning and then repainting. The tyres, still good, are "Firestone". They are not open centre and that is why the farmers do not like them. My greatest pleasure is to look at each part. Each time a parts number comes to mind accompanied by a sweet melody: 1569 - front axle pin; 4153 - radiator cap; 8539 - muffler; 2527 - seat; 2425 - control valve; 7009 - pto shaft... And in spite of all these years my memory has retained many others.

I have also kept in my mind

RALLYE NATIONAL 'FERGUSON' GEMBLOUX 1951
Vce générale
Meeting of about 600 TE-20 coming from all belgian areas

A gathering of 600 TE-20 type tractors which came from all areas of Belgium for the "Rallye National 'Ferguson'" at Gembloux in 1951.

some rather funny incidents:

1949. I found myself at the great fair DLG in Hamburg (Germany) with Mr Lucien Wagner, one of the directors of Maison Impéria. Several TE 20 tractors in grey livery were exhibited in the middle of a crowd of German tractors, gleaming in bright colours. Two officials from the German Ministry of Agriculture arrived and looked with pity at the poor little greys. In reply to their question, "Do they have diesel engines?" Mr Wagner launched into a speech that could not be more favourable to the "Ferguson system". And at the end, in front of two astounded officials, he gave the Nazi salute, shouting "Heil Ferguson!"

The same year, at the Ferguson stand in a Belgium showroom a well-dressed man approached one of the exhibited tractors. He challenged me, "Is the engine vaporising oil?" I replied in the affirmative. He approached again and asked for more information including the price of the tractor. Then, he put his hand on the bonnet of TED 20 and, with a satisfied smile, asked, "Is this one ready for delivery?" I replied, "Probably, I'm not sure". Then he said, "I'll take it." At the same time he grabbed the key of his car and engraved his signature on the surface of the bonnet with the key.

Gérard had bought a TE 20 with a Continental engine. He had been informed that a light consumption of oil by the engine was normal. One day, I went to see him and asked if all was well. He was satisfied, yet he was surprised that the announced oil consumption only occurred in the "forward engine" but there wasn't any in the "rear engine" pointing his finger to the rear axle of the tractor!

The pasture on Gilles's farm was beyond the tramway line. Each morning, Gilles made his way there with his TE 20 equipped with a transport box carrying milk churns for milking his cows. Unfortunately, one morning, Gilles had not taken account of the passing of a tram and, at the moment of crossing the rails, the tram was upon him. With a loud noise of brakes and the horn, the tram slowed down but it was too late. Gilles's tractor was half entangled onto the track. The tram was going fairly slowly at the moment of impact and it ran into the front part of the tractor whose body broke just behind the gearbox. Gilles had stayed on his seat. He was then surprised to see the front of his tractor accompanying the tram on its way – whereas

The Gilles'tractor, few months after the collision with the tram (1951)

The Gilles's tractor a few months after the collision with the tram, 1951.

the rear had fallen forward. Gilles found himself still sitting but with his feet on the ground! He was more frightened than hurt. Thanks to the fast after-sales service performed by Ferguson, Gilles's tractor was repaired and ready to go again two days later. He did not have any more unpleasant encounters.

It was at Stoneleigh Abbey that I met Mr Jean-Jacques Bouillant-Linet, the son of M Bouillant-Linet who was the importer of Ferguson tractors into France. Jean-Jacques followed an "Education course". I have forgotten the name of the instructor who took the course but I remember he had difficulty remembering the name Bouillant-Linet. Therefore it was with much pleasure that I heard him speak of Jean-Jacques "Beaujolais"!

Gustave was a Ferguson enthusiast. Like everybody, the lack of traction of the tractor, without weight on the back, preoccupied him. In his area, the major problem was with the use of manure spreaders. Being a researcher and a good mechanic, Gustave had built a spreader whose direction of operation was reversed. This procedure allowed maintenance of a large quantity of manure in the front part of the spreader which had the result of keeping a maximum of weight on the back of the tractor and therefore obtaining more grip. Alas! In trials it was quickly established that the system was not acceptable. By the mere fact of its idea, the machine set a large load of manure on the back of the tractor and on its unfortunate driver.

Trouble-Shooting with Massey-Ferguson (USA)

Donald R Potter

I started with Massey Ferguson in mid-1959 almost immediately subsequent to the M-H-F period.

My primary duties were to bridge the rift between personnel from the former Massey-Harris and Ferguson companies in the Service and Technical departments responsible for field service advice, owners' and technical manuals and service training. The facility was located in Warren Avenue, Detroit in a building formerly used by the Ford Motor Co. We presented product problems derived from warranty and service reports to Engineering and Manufacturing. Herman Klemm was Chief Engineer for Tractors and he was adamant that percentage failure rates were known to enable prompt rectification actions.

When Albert Thornbrough had become President of M-H-F, his bias to develop the Ferguson style of tractors had become evident with the closure of the Massey-Harris tractor plant at Racine, Wisconsin.

The MF 65 tractor was released almost straight from the drawing board. Fortunately it was successful but it set a precedent of releasing other machines without adequate field testing during development.

The consequences were many resulting in some expensive corrective modification programmes. A particularly expensive one was a failure that occurred on a backhoe loader utility tractor. A regulating spool

From North American archives a prototype styling model for the M-F 65 Tractor. It is uncanny in the way that some of the styling of the later 100 series tractors can be seen in it.

valve encased in the flywheel housing had to be replaced, with forecasts of huge labour expense (millions of dollars!) in removing the mounted equipment and splitting the tractor. Fortunately I conceived an idea to drill a large hole in the bell housing to allow access to the valve. The idea was accepted and I was awarded a sizeable salary increase!

The Massey-Harris and Ferguson amalgamation was not a compatible joining. There was considerable competition within departments. Free exchange of information and co-operation between individuals from the parent companies was practically non-existent. Departmental managers from the two parent companies were trying to remove personnel formally from the other company!

Efforts were made to introduce other products. Lawn equipment and Snowmobiles were designed and manufactured in Wisconsin, These products did not receive adequate promotion by dealers interested in the more profitable larger equipment. A Japanese sourced tractor was also introduced to the product line. The Lundell hay packer that produced small compact hay cubes proved, after considerable expense and effort, to be impracticable. 122 machines were sent to the scrap heap at a cost of 12 or more million dollars. The Lundell Hay Chopper, companion to the Hay Packer, was another outside sourced machine that failed, as also was the Badger Silage Chopper.

The farm market was rapidly moving towards higher powered tractors. The MF 85 and 88 tractors soon followed the MF 65. Due to union domination at the Detroit Tractor Plant quality control was not of the best and as a result Quality Control Manager's releases were blunt about the product problems. The MF 90 and 1100 series tractors followed.

Unfortunately the combine division did not receive adequate research and development funding to remain competitive and dominate the market. The MF share of the market lessened. Early release of a corn head for the MF 35 combine to provide an in field sheller was a classic example of inadequate testing. The MF 35 grain threshing components proved to be not rugged enough for the harsh corn material. A very expensive in field modification programme followed with the product reputation damaged.

In 1961 I was appointed US General Services Manager based in Toronto. During this period a grain swather developed for Western Canada had design problems requiring in field improvement. I had to conspire with the factory and parts manager to pre-build replacement parts before funds were approved!

1964-65 saw considerable expansion of the company. US Sales headquarters moved from Toronto to Des Moines where there also was relocated tillage implement manufacture. Elaborate Service and Product Training was in place on a farm in Indiana. There were four separate facilities in the Detroit area with the establishment of a composite Engineering and Fabrication facility applying the latest computer design to test and manufacture procedural methods of tractor design. The new combine plant in Brantford, Ontario was operating.

In 1965 I moved to Detroit to become Tractor Product Manager in the newly formed Product Integrity Division. Development of articulated four wheel drive tractors followed. The design tolerances of the power shift transmission presented high production costs and in field difficulties.

In 1972 I transferred to the Construction and Industrial at Akron, Ohio. The division was being closed and Industrial Equipment manufacture was returned to the Detroit Southfield plant. The construction equipment market was declining with completion of the inter state highway system and Alaska oil pipeline. The expense of acquiring plants in Italy and Germany producing equipment which was in direct competition with Caterpillar was not an astute move and the division was phased out in the early 1980s.

I retired in 1982 leaving as the Eastern Division Service Manager. The closure of MF's North America Operation (NAO) was soon to follow.

From M-H to MF via M-H-F (Scotland, England, Algeria, Eire, Canada)

Bryan Rogers - May 1948

I joined Massey-Harris as Assistant to Mr. Stangroom, the Works Manager at the M-H Barton Dock Road plant in Manchester. The General Manger was Lionel Harper and the Managing Director George Thomas. At the time the M-H engineering design group was based at the older Ashburton Road, site a mile or two away. The factory was under great pressure as it could sell anything it made to a booming agriculture bereft of new machinery. My first job was to check all planned machine tool loadings for the following six months. This revealed a chaotic overload even without the ongoing addition of work for the new M-H 722* combine which was well behind schedule. I was moved on to "chasing" the parts shortage list on the 722 being assembled at M-H's original site in Ashburton Road. There was a constant stream of last minute items from Barton Dock Road to Ashburton Road. The constant excuse was "lost at Kellogg's factory corner due to spillage from racing lorries." There was chaotic production control – we never knew whether we had completed 399, 400, or 401 machines by the end of August! So much for the 722.

*Note that at the very start of the 722 programme it was known as the 222 – a derivative of the North American M-H 22.

M-H 744PD Tractor 1948-1949

A small number of pre-production tractors were assembled for proving the Racine produced transmissions and bought in U.K. components, including the Perkins P6 tractor version engine and associated parts. This was late 1948-early 1949 at Ashburton Road and close to the Engineering group. I was involved in production listing of components and liaison with Engineering – then based in Ashburton Road. At this time Beans Industries were involved in tooling up to produce the American components which were expensive.

1949

Originally I had been recruited as prospective maintenance engineer for the new Kilmarnock factory but, due to the delay in building, had been used on the production side in Manchester. Early in 1949 they took on a local maintenance engineer as they wanted me to look after the materials supply, stores and receiving department at Kilmarnock which I duly did early in 1949. I also had temporary responsibility for signing on my own labour, transport and customs drawback on tractors exported. All after less than twelve months experience! This was typical in this industry at that time. The original staff had started the Kilmarnock operation in an office above the Saxone shoe shop in the town.

On arriving I found that as a result of factory delay in building, M-H had taken over "Block 8", a row of eight small factories. By knocking down the partitions we started assembly in this building with no windows, services being put in and guards on duty each night. Packing cases were unloaded from lorries down planks using scaffolding pipes. Finished tractors were pulled up a ramp of wheel weights by a friendly Caterpillar driver still digging for the factory. Within a month we progressed from one a week to one a day and I had a desk and a phone! We still had a long way to go to match Ferguson's 400 per day! My motor cycle was parked by my desk. I had also signed on an ex marine commando who put the fear of God into the labourers who soon put together a huge stack of storage bins from old packing cases for the thousands of parts swamping us. As an ex-Navy Engineer Officer familiar with tank landing craft he wanted me to help import black market petrol from the Isle of Arran! I had been warned. He later "sidelined" P6 engines to a garage in Troon. He went!

When the new factory became available and some hundreds of new staff taken on we built up production to about 10-15 a day with difficulties of all sorts. As an example, it had been planned to move tractor components from the docks and tractors for export, in particular by rail. A branch siding had been put in by 1947 from a line 200 yards from the factory. The Act of Parliament necessary for the level crossing to be used by the railway was not passed until 1951!

Standard and rowcrop model 744 tractors were exported mainly to Africa on the groundnut scheme in Tanganyika and also to the Sudan. Finance for

Building of the Kilmarnock factory in progress.

these exports came from the World Bank. Quite a few were sold in the UK. Beans Industries quickly supplanted the expensive American parts by making transmissions and axles. The six cylinder engine was well liked and easily serviced by agents because thousands were in use in road trucks. For export markets an inertia starter was available as an option where tractors could be remote from service facilities and where batteries tended to be "lost"!

Tired of reaching production targets, then having higher ones imposed, plus 80 hour weeks, and losing my job as Chief Maintenance Engineer I joined the new Engineering Department being set up in Block 8 – the building recently vacated.

A Service School Class in session.

Two shots of the M-H School of Service Instruction at the M-H Kilmarnock Factory in Scotland.

The Showroom and Lecture Hall at Kilmarnock.

Engineering Standards

My first job was to set up relevant Engineering drawing standards which I found relatively easy but laborious. Converting S.A.E. and Toronto works standards largely involved steel specifications, thread standards, hole clearances, tolerances, surface finishes, paints, oils and grease etc. where I tried to use B.S. standards wherever possible. This was done within months when I was then given the job of Project Engineer on balers – so avoiding the ensuing arguments with the factory used to Toronto drawings! Little did I know of what lay ahead!

M-H 701 Baler – spectacular failure and eventual success

Some prototypes were assembled from Canadian drawings early in 1950 for test in the UK. These prototypes were late and missed the hay season.

1951

Many mechanical failures were overcome but the knotters were unreliable and lack of experience on my part prevented things being put right. In spite of my personal pleading the Managing Director ordered 1,000 to be built for the 1952 season. Marketing could sell any number and the Canadian designers were happy with Canadian production. Production for 1952 was late – most missing the hay season.

In the meantime we had been making hundreds of changes as a result of intensive testing causing factory disruption. Canadians came over to "put us back on track" – but left agreeing all we had done plus more! In the meantime the early production which baled late hay got into some trouble but the bulk came through the straw season in reasonable shape – hence

A fully automatic twine tying baler, the No. 701 · will effectively handle all types of hay and straw.

An M-H 744D Tractor in action with an M-H 701 Baler. Note the unusual air cleaner arrangement on this particular tractor, and the wheel weights. This is the baler that had knotter problems!

the order for 2000 more for 1953 in spite of the fact that only a small proportion of the engineering changes were adopted. Much of the essence of our problems was that the Canadians dealt with short dry material whereas we usually had long and damp straw and hay.

During this period we tested Coventry Victor petrol/paraffin engines and pto drives to replace the Wisconsin petrol engines which worked well but were expensive to buy and run. The Ferguson tractors operating balers via the pto were not really powerful enough in many conditions.

1953 was disastrous. A large proportion of machines gave more than sufficient trouble. Result – management took the decision to recondition 3,000 machines at Barton Dock Road and still build more machines at Kilmarnock. The President, James Duncan came over to check on what was going on prior to this decision and I met him at a Banbury hotel – duck for lunch! Expecting to be fired I actually got a substantial rise later in the year!

A lot of sleep in late 1953 and early 1954 was on the Glasgow/Manchester sleeper as I was called for in both places. Both factories did a wonderful job and the 1954 season was quite satisfactory. M-H-F got an exceptional level of approval from all our customers and set the standard for the future. No pay rise for me! (It later transpired that Duncan had been over organising the merger with Ferguson – too preoccupied to worry about balers).

Lesson. Take on experienced people and test in all likely crops in all targeted markets before engineering release. Through bitter experience I had gained more 701 baler knowledge than anyone!

M-H 703 Baler

To meet the competition, and provide a smaller, lighter machine to be used with the Ferguson tractor, M-H in Toronto was developing the No. 3 baler. The drawings were received from Canada with some suspicion. This time a number of machines were tested in different countries – including New Zealand (where I spent five months in South Island) with similar hay crops to UK. Various changes were found necessary in different markets but production was achieved more or less on time with few field problems. As markets expanded we had to provide differing pto and hitch standards to suit European tractors in addition to S.A.E. and Ferguson. A relatively small

modern farming's **NEW** pace-setter

MASSEY-FERGUSON

The UK built M-H 703 Baler was based on the Canadian designed M-H 3 Baler shown here in M-F livery.

CX 160 Baler – about 1962

M-F conceived a small baler in about 1962. It was intended to have world-wide application, a key feature being that no component would be more than six feet long in order to facilitate cheap transport around the world. It had a high speed knotter capable of 120 cycles per minute and six prototypes were built. Trials of them were very successful. However there was considerable resistance from M-F in France who had assumed baler production – they were very protective of their small press "baler". Sadly the project was abandoned.

number of J.A.P. petrol and Petter diesel engined machines were tried out with hill farmers who had small tractors.

M-H 704 Baler - 1958

UK Engineering was entrusted with the development of a larger 18" x 16" cross section baler, mainly for the USA and Canadian markets for both twine and wire tie. Huge quantities of hay (wire tied bales) from Arizona and other states was shipped north for Chicago and other stock yards. Arizona conditions allowed as many as 11 cuts per year of alfalfa. Other markets included South Africa (very short crops), possibly Argentina and some for Holland (very long crops). The machine was tested by me in USA, Canada, South Africa and Holland as by this time I had a good design staff and test engineers to put field experience into good drawings. Various markets approved the machinery, it was released, partly tooled, but never went into production due to industrial problems at Kilmarnock which ultimately resulted in baler production moving to France (in the much smaller Lille factory) which put paid to balers, due to cost, within a few years. The baler was designed for a 65 hp tractor and provision was designed in for engine drive but never tested on the three or four prototypes which were made.

M-H 735 Combine

The machine was originally designed in Toronto for the European market – particularly for the family farms of Germany and France, and for narrow lane parts of Devon for example. The machine was redrafted at Eschwege in Germany for German production and I took over the re-drafting at Kilmarnock for production there. It was fragile, under-powered and unstable on steep slopes. We thought it wouldn't compete with second hand M-H 722s or 726s in UK and the market agreed. Far easier to put up wider gates!

M-H 750 Combine – about 1952

Sample machines and drawings were received from M-H in Racine, Wisconsin and a Kilmarnock built version went into production for the short straw markets of Europe such as Greece and also North Africa where Racine built machines were too expensive. It was only built in limited numbers. It was a pull behind machine for larger tractors and I venture to suggest that those who bought it in N.W. Europe probably regretted it!

Right: The M-H 745S Tractor was the last M-H Tractor produced in the UK and the final version of the 745. In contrast to the 744s and 745 it had a truck type chassis rather than cast frame. It was made in general purpose, standard and hi-arch form.

Far right: The features that made the M-H 745 S different.

M-H 745 Tractor

The Chief Engineer on this project, Pat Mulholland was a close friend of mine. (I modified, in his barn, a 6.5 litre Bentley to take an ex factory Perkins P6 diesel!) Management required drastic cost reductions – hence the 4 cylinder Perkins L4 diesel engine to replace the P6, and poor front axles of the subsequent 745 tractor. Both these major changes gave trouble in the tough hard ground and dusty, poorly serviced areas of Africa. The 745 had to give way to the more up to date Ferguson design tractors.

Ferguson Side Mounted Implements

I was on the evaluation team for the baler which was cumbersome, far too wide, under-powered and impractical. In many cases the farmer wanted his tractor for other purposes during harvest. I believe the combine and forager had the same conceptual problem. The evaluation of the baler took place in Canada; the combine in UK and the USA, and I think the forager only in North America.

The semi-mounted hitch on the baler was easy to use and the machine worked well in dry crops on hard ground conditions. Steering was a severe problem on soft ground, the machine slewing round on the outer

baler wheel. Later, a baler drive wheel kit became available to overcome this problem. The overall width was not acceptable in Canada and would have been totally unacceptable in the UK. Tractor power was inadequate under adverse conditions.

I had nothing to do with testing the combine other than once seeing it working in Warwickshire. H R Jenner, my boss, was a man of great integrity and experience and was entrusted with testing the machine for M-H-F. He pronounced against it on grounds of slowness, poor visibility and accessibility, and lack of power. At this time it was no match for a second-hand self-propelled machine in terms of power and cost – as was also the 735 combine.

I saw the forager in Canada but not at work. Being Project Manager on evaluation of out sourced machines in the UK (we used Lundell at the time) I would have guessed that the machine was vastly under powered especially if a trailer was towed behind.

I was of the opinion that Mr. Ferguson was allowing development of the machines to go ahead, designers were gaining experience, and on the assumption that more powerful tractors would answer the power problems. Of course mounted engines did become available as an option.

Both the USA built Ferguson Side-Mounted Forager and Baler could be fitted with a drive wheel kit. A drive was taken from the tractor rear wheel to the wheel on the implement as shown on this Forage Harvester.

The Massey-Harris and Ferguson Merger, and Beyond

In theory after rationalisation it should have been a good merger – and to some extent was. Note:

- The Ferguson system was great – for small tractors.
- The Ferguson implements were on the whole quite good but vastly costly in relation to the more blacksmith orientated opposition. Polish aircraft engineers produced some beautiful designs to aircraft standards – and costs. I was in charge of all MF implement design in 1966 or thereabouts but by 1972 all implement design except for seed drills and rotary mowers ceased, due largely to large overheads, subcontract costs and better added value with tractors.
- The larger Ferguson tractor was beautifully designed but hopelessly expensive in relation to Ford for example.
- The Ferguson tractor itself was expensive – Standard Motors had to be bought out!
- The merger suffered the usual political warfare for some years. Many good distributors across the world were lost and eventually the concentration of financial strength in Detroit destroyed combine development in Toronto and we effectively lost that market leadership.
- The exorbitant cost of the larger Ferguson and poor Detroit designs made things difficult for many years. I took over development of tractors in Coventry in 1972-78, and design except for transmission – still using large parts of the Banner Lane transfer line laid down for the original grey Fergie in the 1940s.
- Huge sums of money were lost by Detroit by trying to "beat Caterpillar in five years" with colossal development cost of their Industrial and

Construction Equipment business in Germany and USA. This, and the sudden stop by the World Bank of aid to the Middle East where we had very large markets, made things very difficult.

It was hardly surprising that some animosity occurred between two highly successful companies with different traditions and areas of experience. By the early 1950s Ferguson's high manufacturing costs due to subcontracting and lack of manufacturing experience meant that the writing was on the wall as far as profitability was concerned. Also they had no harvesting equipment to talk of, no large "big farm" equipment or experience. Massey-Harris on the other hand had no up to date tractors or plants to make them in Europe but did have a range of harvesting equipment including leadership in the combine market, big farm experience and factories in many parts of the world. Massey were right I think to take over Ferguson, buy the Banner Lane facilities and later Perkins engines. I don't think Mr. Ferguson had any other option.

On the implement side of Massey's I was very much aware of and admired the Ferguson System. On the whole the merger proved a success in spite of losing many good men and distributors on the way.

My work overseas

Most of it related to the above. I travelled widely in Europe with occasional visits to North Africa, and Italy concerned with combines. Why the latter I don't really know as my knowledge was very limited, but Tom Carroll, the renowned inventor of the self-propelled combine occasionally liked me on his team. Here are a few memories:

Ireland 1952. The Irish dealer wanted "the baler specialist" to start up the first 701 baler in Ireland. Rain was expected so the engine-driven machine was set up in a very small yard on one side of which was a hay stack to be hand-fed into the machine. After the first bale everything stopped for a celebration making full use of some long-necked Irish bottles! Ditto for the second and third bales!

North Africa 1952. While combining testing in Algeria with particular reference to abrasive dust problems, the M-H Oran branch manager, knowing some officials at the Sidi bell Abbess HQ of the French Foreign Legion, had arranged for us to visit the strongly guarded complex. Flourishing our passes we approached and started to enter the gates only to be suddenly surrounded by fierce looking Legionnaires. There had been an insurrection earlier that morning! Profuse apologies in broken French and waving of passes and passports allowed the guns to be lowered and we slunk back to Oran.

Western Canada 1955. When travelling between baler test sites, I landed up rather late in Fort Macleod. This was one of those isolated stockades to defend the pioneers against the Indians, and was still a rather backward place! Only a "bunkhouse" had accommodation at one dollar a night. It consisted of twelve compartments each with a hard bunk with straw palliases and the facilities consisted of a bucket each, a cold tap and basin for all of us. Stuck on the wall was a water-splashed notice beside the filthy towel reading "any complaints to the manager"! He was about 6 ft. 3 in. and at a guess some 16 stone. No chance of a clean towel! Another notice said "use the bucket and remove spurs before bunking". We Massey boys knew some high living!

Take it in your Stride! (USA)

Don Snyder

My father became a Massey-Harris dealer in 1951 when I was a junior in high school. Our dealership name was Snyder Tractor and Auto Service and was later changed to our current name, Snyder Equipment Inc. My father sent me to Massey-Harris service school at Detroit, Michigan, in 1952 and I still have my notes taken at the school. I did repair work in our shop and in the summer time I did custom baling and combining with a Massey-Harris 44 tractor, No. 1 baler, and Clipper pull type combine.

Being a Massey-Harris dealer we had to be convinced that the Massey-Harris model 50, Ferguson style, tractor was going to be a sellable tractor, as we were used to the big Massey-Haris tractors. As for the Ferguson dealers, they were not happy with the Massey-Harris dealers having a hi-clearance Massey-Harris model 50 to sell. Plus, they only had the standard models to sell. Therefore, in 1956, the Ferguson model 40 was made for them to sell in standard, hi-clearance, tricycle, and single front-end styles. They were also able to sell the Massey-Harris Pony model painted Ferguson grey.

We sold Massey Harris tractors, ploughs, harrows, discs, cultivators, mowers, rakes, pull type and self-propelled balers, and combines. We also serviced and repaired equipment and carried a lot of parts. The merger did not affect us too much, as we took it in our stride!

Agricultural Engineer (UK)

Alan Starley

Alan Starley demonstrating a TE 20 type tractor with three furrow plough.

Alan Starley joined M-H-F in 1953. The son of a glasshouse nurseryman, he at one time worked for the National Institute of Agricultural Engineering and always held a deep conviction that he wanted to work for Harry Ferguson in particular and farm machinery in general. An early desire to be a wheelwright was never fulfilled; he came across his first Ferguson TE 20 tractor whilst working on a market garden – his first job. Whilst working for the NIAE he met Ferguson's Polish test engineer who supervised the testing of Ferguson tractors which were submitted to the OECD test there. This was his first contact with the Ferguson organisation. On the basis of this he wrote to Harry Ferguson Ltd. asking for a job and was interviewed by Jack Bibby, the Field Test manager whose boss was Eric Somerfield who was in charge of the implement drawing office. Alan was appointed as a Field Test driver. He recalls that when he joined M-H-F in 1953 it was still very much a Ferguson organisation and change was very gradual.

Opposite far left: A prototype M-H-F 45 Tractor was made. 15-20 of them are thought to have been tested. Essentially it was an LPG (liquefied petroleum gas) version of the Ferguson 40/M-H 50 type tractors. This is an M-H 50 type and serial number SGM 404220

Opposite left: This surviving Ferguson 40 type, M-H-F 45 example is serial number SHM 408686 fitted with Continental engine SN Zb134 657819. This engine is a high compression version of the Z 134 engine used on both high altitude and LPG models.

An early job was working on the field familiarisation and evaluation of a Ferguson side-mounted forage harvester which had been brought over from North America. This was mounted on the new TO-35 tractor. The forager was fitted with its own power unit (Continental engine as fitted in North American Ferguson tractors). Alan worked on this machine with Dick Dowdeswell at a farm in Southam, Warwickshire. It had a reciprocating blade cutter bar. From this the crop was conveyed to a multi-bladed cylindrical chopping unit and subsequently blown into the transporting trailer. The chopping unit had a sharpening device and so allowed routine maintenance to keep a keen cutting edge on this vital component. Alan described it as a very good machine with ample power – the power unit ran at full revs. However it never came onto the U.K market. He recalls it working in a tall experimental crop which may have been of the artichoke specie.

Alan did a little field work on the LTX tractor. He says it had very good traction but with heavy steering. He also recalls that Alec Moor and Bill Harrow, former Daimler engine engineers had a large input into the design of the LTX engines. Apparently the famous diesel engine consulting engineers Ricardo deemed the engine to be PERFECT! Alan comments that possibly the LTX engine was the only one of the day that had been specifically designed for a tractor and the type of work it would encounter. All other tractor manufacturers – even Ferguson – were using engines originally developed for industrial or transport applications. Could the LTX have been sold at a profit? Could it have competed on price with the Fordson Major diesel? Could the supply and sale of larger implements have been geared up in time? These are valid and profound questions which Alan raises.

He worked much overtime on field testing. They were always busy testing all over the U.K. Much time was spent seeking out farmers who had large areas of land available to plough or cultivate. He spent two years on field tests and then moved into the drawing office at Fletchamstead. This followed several years of part-time study for his engineering Higher National Diploma. In many ways he was the odd one out. He had a solid background in agricultural field mechanisation practice – an "agricultural" engineer – whereas most other staff in the drawing office had generally a motor car engineering background.

Working on the design of the Ferguson sugar beet harvester under George Holmes, the Design Office section leader for this machine was also an illuminating experience. One day whilst demonstrating a prototype at Stoneleigh he caught the elevator on a tree – not too much damage except to the ego! The senior man on the spot asked, "do you do much tractor driving?" The harvester was designed to take its depth control from the Ferguson System but in the event the machine was too heavy and long for this to work effectively as on a normal short Ferguson implement. In truth the TE 20 type tractor was probably too small for the machine. Finally depth wheels had to be fitted – against all Ferguson principles! This resulted in there being no weight transfer upon which the TE 20 depended – a definite disadvantage in wet autumn sugar beet fields.

Another prototype machine with which Alan worked was a Ferguson rotavator. This had a central drive to the rotor which meant that the machine did not cultivate a narrow central strip! It failed to reach production.

Ferguson had much higher drawing office standards than Massey-Harris. Ferguson had a "drawing office standards" manual to work to. Apparently Harry Ferguson had instigated this as a result of his observations on how Henry Ford operated. Another fundamental difference in approach to design was that Ferguson always built prototypes to production standards whereas Massey-Harris did it very much by trial and error with a "can you try that" and "can you

weld that on" approach! The essence of the famed Ferguson high strength and lightness of implements was that he used heat-treated steel. This meant that strength could be doubled or trebled for the same thickness – but it cost money.

Various manuals were used to obtain a co-ordinated level of design throughout the drawing office. Suitable steel specification and any heat treatment required was specified to the project engineers by the resident metallurgist. Material for each component of each implement had to have the approval of the metallurgist. Likewise any field failure was always subject to the metallurgist's examination. The co-ordination and documentation of drawings for "release to production" was also first class. Prior to release for production of any new product there was an engineering checking process for each component and overall fit, thus giving co-ordination and continuity to all designs. This checking was carried out by a separate group of draughtsmen headed by a project engineer. This was an important procedure to avoid any costly errors before tooling was laid down for full-scale production. Ferguson really was an efficient set-up in all departments. Alan was fascinated by all this engineering organisation and activity. "What a time in the Ferguson history to have been at the heart of it all! I often wondered what it might have been like when the Ford Ferguson project first got under way?" says Alan.

The Ferguson drawing office was an expensive facility to run, but it was a quality one. This is very much the Ferguson experience that M-H had wanted to acquire as much as the Ferguson System. Again Alan draws a comparison – Ferguson was engineering oriented whereas Massey-Harris was more sales oriented. Ferguson also had a dedicated demonstration team because his ideas were so new. Massey-Harris took a more ad hoc approach.

Alan eventually moved out of the drawing office to become a Product Planner in the early 1960s. "The knowledge I gained in the engineering environment proved to be an invaluable aid as a Product Planner," he says. The objective of product planners was to keep factories running at full production which in turn means making the right product. In this role he came to regard himself as an "Engineering Agronomist". The concept of "World-Wide Product Planning" came out of the merger and Alan regards it as possibly one of the finer things to come out

The Ferguson Kale Cutrake.

of it. Potential products had to be looked at on a world-wide basis. One had to look at the product from an international viewpoint, get the product to the customer at an affordable price. Fundamental questions had to be asked from many angles and involving different disciplines in the whole concept/design/production/marketing chain. Fundamental questions could be as basic as asking "do we need to plough?" In other words look at the logic of each component of the whole chain.

One of his first endeavours as a product planner was the CX 117 seed drill. Here the concept was to have weight transfer from a seed drill. Wheels were placed behind the drill at the rear of the hopper. In this way the drill effectively tipped forward its weight on to the tractor hitch. Also the drill had a sowing width equal to the machine's total width, and thereby also a minimum transport width. Alan had wanted a swan neck drawbar to facilitate tight pivotal headland turns but cost implications vetoed this idea. This drill was one of the first products to come from product planning and not, as before, from engineering. CX 117 failed to reach production.

Bryan Rogers additionally comments that the small wheels were unsatisfactory as they caused compaction, had a high rolling resistance and made loading of grain and fertiliser difficult. Subsequently the design was modified to side wheels and the drill designated

as the CX 253. In production it became the MF 30 drill which had a wide range of variable specifications and was in production for many years.

Alan had some involvement with the Kale Cutrake. This was a farmer's idea, a Mr Gale, but few were sold – probably a reflection of rapidly changing cropping practice on farms with kale going out of favour.

Two other brief memories of Alan's: Firstly some design of the M-H 745 tractor and emergency chassis modifications on the 745S were made at Fletchamstead in "Ferguson" territory. Secondly he saw what looked like water being poured into the oil filler point on a TEA 20 tractor destined for the Antarctic crossing. On enquiry it turned out to be SAE 5 oil. Sewing machine grade?!

Alan's abiding image of Harry Ferguson is that he was the "Master Product Planner". He says it is a credit to his character that he enabled people to produce the designs he wanted, and surmises that the key that defines Harry Ferguson's success must surely have been his man-management skills and abilities. Since Alan injured his back in his youth whilst attempting to hitch up a single axle trailer to a standard Fordson tractor, he has often reflected that if Harry Ferguson had achieved nothing else but the automatic pick-up hitch, then he would have qualified for a place of honour in life's hall of fame!

A few Memories (UK)

Colin Steventon

Colin Steventon was involved with the development of a prototype Ferguson sugar beet harvester – a project that was eventually shelved. He went to Yugoslavia to try and promote the machine there.

He recalled the LTX tractor as being exceptionally powerful even without the use of the three point linkage and hydraulics. He described both the engine and hydraulics as being very powerful. During its development it was used for clearing a lot of bush and it excelled at this. However he described it as a "pig" to drive with awkward steering. Colin also remembered the Ferguson Kale cutrake being introduced and it not being overly successful, whereas the earth scoop became very popular.

The digging end of the prototype Ferguson Beet Harvester.

From Armaments to Industrials (USA)

Roy K Stuart

Roy K Stuart has a unique story to tell. He worked on Massey-Harris armaments production both during and after the war – remember that Massey-Harris still had defence contracts at the time of the merger with Ferguson. Later he had experience of Massey-Harris industrial tractors made for the military followed by involvement in the very early days of M-H-F and M-F industrial equipment. Roy recalls:

The Track Link Line

The first military contract Massey-Harris in Racine got was in 1941 for making links for the tracks for Army tanks. The links held the section of track together and was the part that interlocked with drive sprockets on the front of the vehicle track to power the tank movement. I graduated from High School in June of 1942 and secured a job at Massey-Harris on the link line. I was taught to operate many different machines the year I worked there.

In July of 1943 I enlisted in the Army Airforce Cadet program. I passed the written tests and took the physical examination and went home to wait for my orders to report to be inducted in the Army Airforce. One week later I got a letter indicating that the X-ray showed a spot on one of my lungs. They directed me to report back in three months to see if the spot had disappeared. When I went back to the Army Airforce doctors the X-ray showed the spot was still there. They turned me down classing me as a 4F. I didn't want to go back to the link line!

Testing the Tanks

I talked to a friend who told me that the US Army Ordnance was hiring inspectors for the Massey-Harris Tank plant. I submitted an application and was hired by the US Army Ordnance, Fifth Corp located in Chicago and assigned to the Milwaukee Regional Office, which in turn assigned me to the Massey-Harris Tank plant as a Receiving Room Inspector. The supplies came through this area for verification

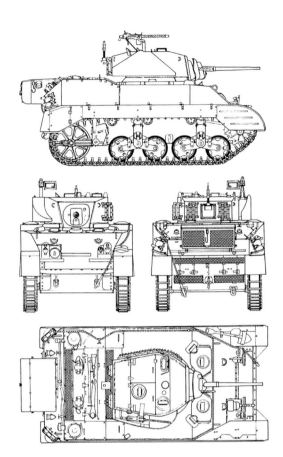

Variations of the Culin hedgerow cutters that were manufactured from old German beach obstructions are seen here. The device was designed to allow a tank to cut through the dense hedges in the Normandy farm country. Note also the well sand-bagged glacis plate which served to protect the M5A1 from German Panzerfaust and Panzerschreck rocket weapons. (US Army)

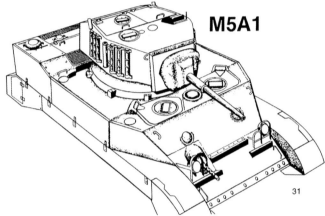

M5A1

Details of the M5A1 Tank and an adaptation for it.

and checking. I stayed there for about six months and after that I found out that there was an opening for a test driver of the M5A1 light tanks that Massey-Harris was building and submitted a request for a transfer to that position, which was accepted. The chief of Road Test put me through about a one month training course before I was able to start testing tanks. The test consisted of about a twenty mile run around a ¾ mile test track located about four blocks from the plant. Once a month we would take a tank and go out on the highway around Racine County and put 500 miles on the vehicle. The tanks were equipped with rubber track sections, so we did not damage any of the roads we travelled. We had a German Prison Camp on Highway 11 in Sturtevant, I loved driving by that place several times on these 500 mile drives.

We had a check list to go over and mark down okay for each item, or mark fail, and list the discrepancies. The tanks were equipped with two side by side 1941

Cadillac V8 automotive gas engines, rated at 210 HP at 2200 RPM, they faced the back of the tank. Attached to those engines were Cadillac Hydra-Matic transmissions which in turn were connected to a transfer case which combined the power of both engines to one output drive shaft. This ran forward and connected to the input shaft on a GM Allison Transmission located at the front of the tank hull between the two drivers. The transmission had two out drive shafts connected to the final drive which in turn connected to the sprockets at the front of the track. The tank was steered by two handle controls located in front of both drivers anchored just below and forward of the hatch doors. They were connected to the Allison transmission which had band brakes which, when one applied pressure to one side, it would slow up and the other side would continue at the same speed, that is how the tank was steered. To stop the tank, both handles would be pulled back.

The self-propelled 155 mm. howitzer, M44, made at the Company's Racine, Wisconsin, plant under contract for the United States Army Ordnance Corps.

For the Canadian Government special engineering development work has been undertaken as well as the production of mortar bombs which are made at Brantford.

Massey-Harris made both tanks and the munitions for various uses.

Making the Tanks

In the summer of 1942 Massey-Harris was awarded a contract to build US Army M5A1 light tanks. The company leased a factory located at 1721 Packard Avenue in Racine. The plant – The Nash Automobile Co. - had been closed since 1940. The GM Cadillac Division was the prime contractor for the M5 A1 Light Tank and later on the M24A1 light tank. The design of these tanks was an evolution from earlier designs of the Stuart family of US Army light tanks, the M2A and the M3A1. This series of tanks was not named after me! – but after Jeb Stuart, a famous Cavalry General from the Civil War. The M5A1 had hydraulic controls for the turret reversing (swinging it around) and for elevating and lowering the 37 mm cannon. It was also equipped with two 30 calibre machine guns. One could be mounted on top of the turret - the gunner fired the weapon standing up in the hatch opening. The other 30 calibre machine gun was mounted in front of the auxiliary driver's position. The 37 mm cannon had a gyroscope mounted to it to help keep the gun on target while travelling across country. I never felt they did any good. However I saw in Desert Storm that on the M1 tanks they worked beautifully. I guess it only took forty years to really develop the gun gyroscope! Production of the M5A1 tanks at Massey-Harris got started in early 1943. The Heil Company in Milwaukee fabricated the hulls and turrets, Renner Mfg Co., Green Bay built the lower gun mounts. The gun and gun mount were furnished by the US Army Ordnance Arsenal. Kelsey Hayes supplied all of the wheels and sprockets. Monroe Auto supplied the shock absorbers, Goodyear supplied the track, Hobbs supplied the instrument panels, Dana the transfer box and drive shafts, Allison the transmissions and final drives. Cadillac supplied the engines and the Hydra-Matic transmissions, Modine supplied the radiators. The guns came from one of the US arsenals, which one I don't remember. Massey-Harris machined the hull and also the turret ring for the large roller bearing, on which the turret rested.

The manufacturing and assembly of the M5A1 and later the M24A1 took place in what is called Building 1000. The production of the M5A1 was stopped in May of 1944, the total number built by the two companies was 6810. The M24A1 was put into production at both Cadillac and Massey-Harris. The design was again done at Cadillac Motors in Detroit, Michigan. The shape of the M24A1 set the tone for most tanks that have followed. The surface of the hull is angled to deflect incoming shells. The suspension system was modernized, and that basic design has been carried forward into the later designed tanks. It had the same engines and drive train as the M5A1.

The big difference was its weapons. It was equipped with an M5 75 mm light weight cannon which had been developed for use on the B25 Mitchell Bomber. It fired the same shells as the M4 Medium tank. The main difference was the barrel on the M24A1 was shorter. The shells' penetration was not as great as the longer barrel cannon. The M24A1 stayed in production until January 1946. I couldn't find a record of how many were built. I guess it would be around 500 to 1000. They started to be delivered to the forces in Europe in late 1944 and saw action in Italy and Germany. They were well received by the US troops. When the Korean War started the M24A1 was the only tank we had over there. Based on the history of that war, they made a good showing. After the war the US Army replaced the M24A1 with the M25 tank. Many of the M24A1 were given over to some of our NATO and Allied countries and saw service for many years with them. That served as fitting testimony to the quality of its design. The M5A1 light tanks were dropped from the US Army inventory after World War Two.

Light Tank M24

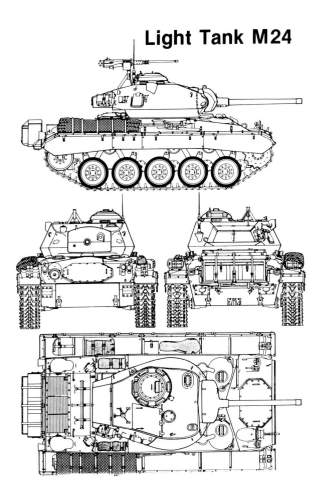

Details of the M24 Tank.

Reconditioning

During early 1944 Massey-Harris received another US army contract to upgrade 250 M10A1 self-propelled gun carriages being returned from the North Africa Campaign of 1942 and 1943. These units were completely disassembled. The 500 HP V8 engines were returned to Ford Motor Company to be recommissioned, and the same thing with the Allison transmissions and drive trains. All the parts were cleaned, inspected and reworked if needed. These gun carriages were rebuilt into M36 self-propelled gun carriages. They were equipped with new open turrets and we installed 90 mm cannons in place of the 76 mm cannons they had. The 90 mm cannon was designed as an anti-aircraft gun. The M36 with this 90 mm cannon was the first gun that the Americans had that would out-shoot the famous German 88 mm cannon. The first M36 gun carriages were shipped to Europe in October of 1944. Some were used in relieving the troops under siege in the Battle of the Bulge. It got the nickname of the Tiger Tamer, because it could destroy the famous German Tiger tank which had the 88 mm cannon.

Peacetime Production

In early 1946, both companies went back into peacetime production of automobiles at Cadillac and tractors, combines and other farm implements at Massey-Harris.

I left the Army Ordinance in January 1946. In early 1951 I read in the local paper that Massey-Harris had been awarded a contract by the US Army to build the M41 155 mm Howitzer self-propelled gun carriage. Pacific Car and Foundry in Washington State was the main contractor for this family of self-propelled gun carriages. The article also stated that Freeman Schoaf would be the Residence Inspector for the US Army Ordinance at Massey-Harris on this contract. Freeman had been the Assistant Resident Inspector at Massey-Harris during World War II and I had reported to him in my position as Chief of Road Testing. I called Freeman to ask him if he would consider me for the position of Chief of Road Testing. He said sure, but he would like to have me consider the position of Assistant Resident Inspector under him. The position worked out great, I ended up having seventeen inspectors reporting to me. Massey-

Harris did the same type of work, machining the hulls and assembling the vehicles. Most suppliers were the same companies as in the War. The engines used were a 500 HP flat six piston air-cooled aircraft type engine furnished by Continental Motors. The contract called for 350 vehicles. They started out with enclosed turrets to protect the crews from atomic bomb radiation fall out. The noise and the concussion from firing the 155 mm Howitzer was so bad that it was decided to cut off the top of the turret! This contract lasted until 1956.

Military Tractors

MASSEY HARRIS and THE MILITARY

In 1953 Massey Harris delivered the I-162 to the U.S. Army. This was the first of five different models of Massey Harris Tractors manufactured for the United States Military.

The I-162 was a 30 hp F-162 Continental. Total weight was 5,300 lbs. It was painted Army Green. The primary use was as a service tractor, pulling equipment. Only 25 of these tractors were made. As of this date only 5 are known to exist. Two in Missouri, one in Illinois, one in Wisconsin and one in Maryland.

In 1954 Massey delivered 6, I-330 Tractors to the Navy. These were 6 cylinder 330 cubic inch continentals. Approximately 60 hp. The I-330 had dual rear tires. Shipping weight was 8,920 lbs. It was painted Battleship Gray.

This tractors primary use was as a service tractor pulling equipment and airplanes. Serial # 1 & 2 were shipped to Fallon, Nevada, Serial #'s 3, 4, & 6 were shipped to Miramar - San Diego, California. Serial # 5 was shipped to Weeksville - Elizabeth City, North Carolina.

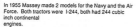

In the fall of 2001 in Lower California, serial #'s 3,4, & 6 were sold at a government surplus sale. Two of the tractors were bought by a scrap dealer and one was bought by a private owner. The other three tractors may still be out there somewhere.

In 1955 Massey made 2 models for the Navy and the Air Force. Both tractors were I-244, both had 244 cubic inch continental engines.

During the life of this contract Massey-Harris was also bidding on government tractor and accessories contracts with the different military services. Schoaf assigned me the added responsibility of the Commanding Officer representative. In this position I had to see that the tractors met the terms of the contracts Massey-Harris had won. They had to put in special engines approved by the different agencies in the military services, the engines had to be radio suppressed (no electrical noise from engines allowed). That is how they came up with the different models, the I 244 G stood for Industrial Tractor with a 244 inch displacement engine and the G was for the Government. The same followed through for the other model tractors they sold to the government. The contract called for the tractors to start at 25 degrees below zero. Prototype tractors were tested in the cold room at the Nash Automobile Plant in Kenosha, Wisconsin. They also had to operate in temperatures of up to 130 degrees. These tests were run in the hot room at Modine in Racine. They also had to meet some minimum slippage test related to the tractor hp.

Start Up of M-H-F Industrials

When the M41 contract was coming to an end in the summer of 1956, I started to think about what was I going to do after this job was over. I read in the paper that the Massey-Harris-Ferguson Industrial Division was advertising for a Sales Correspondent. I asked around what is the Industrial Division and what is a Sales Correspondent. I was told that the Industrial Division was a one-man show and his name was Bernie Berman. Well, that is the guy I had to deal with on those Massey-Harris Government tractor contracts and it was explained to me what a sales correspondent did. I figured I could handle that position and maybe the Industrial Division will grow and it could be a great opportunity for me. I contacted Bernie and told him I was interested in the job. He said if you want it, hell it's yours. So I became the number two employee of the Massey-Harris-Ferguson Industrial Division!

Above left: Roy Stuart wrote this article on the M-H military tractors. It is reproduced here by kind permission.

Left: Roy K. Stuart tests a Ferguson TO 35 fitted with a Front Mounted Road Brush.

Early days of M-F Industrial Equipment. A show breakthrough at one of M-F's first Industrial and Construction Machinery Conventions.

In the early fifties people started hanging loaders and back hoes on the TO 30 and later the TO 35 Ferguson tractors. This caused early failure of front end adjustable axles on those tractors. Some back hoes caused the transmission cases to crack and fail due to no external support of these attachments. Al Thornbrough was looking for some place in the new organization for Bernie. They decided to give Bernie the responsibility of fixing the problems being caused by the new applications which the Ferguson tractors were being put to. This in time led to the start of the Industrial Division which Bernie ended up running.

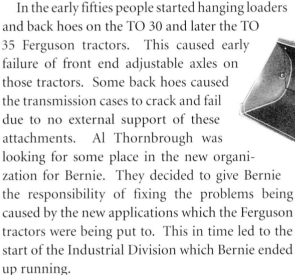

Top: Even the Ferguson TO 35 Tractors became M-H-F Work Bulls. Note the rigid front axle.

Above: Davis 101 and 201 Utility Loaders respectively fitted on to an M-H 50 and Ferguson TO 35 Tractor.

Left: A Wills Ditcher fitted to a British Ferguson Tractor and officially approved by Ferguson.

A 1957 Davis Hydraulic Loader on a Ferguson 40 Tractor.

Bernie went on to make a deal with Chuck Davis, owner of Midwest Industries in Wichita, Kansas. They manufactured the first box construction front end tractor loader. The deal with Davis was that they would only sell mounting kits of their front end loaders for Massey-Harris and Ferguson tractors to M-H-F dealers. Davis had a design for a back hoe but needed help to pay for the tooling involved to mass produce the back hoe. Bernie got M-H-F to loan Davis $200,000.00 for that project. It became known as the 185 Back Hoe. The number stood for the number of degrees the back hoe would swing. For the loan M-H-F got a three-year option to buy Mid West Industries, which they did buy in 1957 for $3,000,000 dollars.

Early in June of 1956 the Industrial Division had a big coming out party for the US Construction Industry

Press at Bloom Acres in Sturtevant, Wisconsin. Bloom Acres was a gentleman farm owned by H. Bloom. We had developed a trade mark of a fighting bull to indicate the strength of the products. Several of the press people suggested we change the name of the division to the Work Bull Division which we did. The name of M-H-F got shortened in 1959 to Massey-Ferguson Inc. We introduced the following equipment at the 1956 show:

The M-H-F Work Bull logo used on M-H and Ferguson tractors adapted for industrial use.

MF 202. Standard Ferguson TO 35 or MF 35 tractor painted yellow with solid front axle and power steering and industrial tires.

MF 203. The same as the MF 202 but with a diesel engine.

MF 204. The same as the MF 202 but with a Borg and Beck Torque converter and a Funk forward and reverse transmission behind the torque convertor. No shifting was required. The movement was controlled by a foot pedal which was also the throttle.

MF 205. The same as the MF 204 but with a diesel engine.

Two loaders for these tractors, the 101 and 102 loaders. The 101 had one cylinder on the bucket tilt whereas the 102 had two.

The 185 back hoe was also shown on these tractors.

We also showed an MB front mounted broom for these tractors, and an Evert trencher mounted on an MF 202 tractor. This was a large wheel type trencher mount on the back end, with scoop type shovels mounted on the wheel. The drive for the trencher was a thin gearbox fitted in behind the clutch case and in front of the differential case. It had a drive on the side which connected to the wheel drive.

We showed an MF 303 tractor, which was made up on an M-H 333 chassis with engine, radiator and accessories, and with a new sheet metal body and industrial tires. The operator was moved forward and higher on the tractor. We showed this with the large 500 loader mounted on it.

Also shown was the MF 303 Shovel loader, which had the same chassis as the MF 303 but the tractor was operated backwards. The operator sat between the large tires facing the loader mounted to what was the back of the MF 333 chassis. The loader for this shovel loader was made up from the 500 loader. This unit also had the torque converter and the Funk forward and reversing transmission.

We showed a Ram portable self-contained street sweeper that mounted to the 500 loader or the shovel loader in place of the bucket.

Moving to Wichita

After Massey-Harris-Ferguson exercised their option to buy Midwest Industries in the spring of 1957, M-H-F moved the Industrial Division to Wichita. Chuck Davis agreed to stay on as the General Manager. I went from Racine to Wichita as the US Merchandise Distribution Manager. My responsibilities were scheduling production of loaders and back hoes and their accessories in the Wichita plant and the production of the industrial tractors and their options out of the Detroit, Michigan plant. We received and processed all sales orders and issue releases to the factories for shipments. The Shipping Department answered to my department.

Chuck Davis resigned in 1959. He told me that he didn't mind fighting competitors, but he didn't like guarding his back! Charles Hill, who had closed the Racine Plant came down as the General Manager. Having Chuck Davis no longer in charge, Detroit was able to convince M-F management that they could save money by moving the production and engineering to Detroit and the Marketing group to Toronto, Ontario, Canada. I had young kids and didn't want to move to Canada.

So I moved to Cessna Fluid Power Division located in Hutchinson, Kansas who were the major hydraulic product supplier of pumps, cylinders, control valves and filters to MF Industrial Division at Wichita and sold cylinders to MF Toronto for the Model 72-82 and 92 self-propelled combines. One of my major accounts was to be MF in North America. Cessna eventually located another plant in Glenroth, Scotland to supply the British and European M-F markets.

The oldest of Recollections
(Italy, Egypt, Mali, Senegal, Sudan, Turkey, Iraq)

Charles Voss

Getting Started

I must be one of the oldest surviving employees from the Massey-Harris side, having joined the company as a junior clerk on December 1st, 1929 at the age of 18 in Budapest. After the war I joined the European Export department as assistant sales manager, which in 1946 was based on the French factory at Marquette-lez Lille, before moving to Berkeley Square in London in 1950. My links with M-H actually go back further than this because my father was the M-H European Export Sales manager under James Duncan and based at Marquette. When James Duncan moved to

Left: Charles demonstrating an M-H 12-20 tractor in 1929 near Vienna.

Below: A 40 year celebration reunion of senior M-H management in Vienna, 1930. Charles's father Mr S. S. Voss 3rd from left, James Duncan 4th from left, George Thomas from UK 5th from left, W Lattman 7th from left joint manager in Berlin.

Appointed Assistant to European Export Sales Manager

CHARLES VOSS

Announcement has been made by Mr. G. H. Thomas of the appointment of Mr. Charles Voss to the position of Assistant to the European Export Sales Manager at Paris, France.

His services with the company dates back to 1929 when he entered the service of the branch at Budapest and later Berlin office and the Marquette factory. In 1932 he was transferred to Manchester and has been blockman at Manchester since 1938.

Mr. Voss is the son of the late Mr. S. S. Voss, former European General Manager who, at the outbreak of war remained behind in Europe to look after the company's interests, was subsequently arrested by the enemy and lost his life in a German concentration camp.

January 1947.

Toronto before the war, my father then became acting European General Manager, but he was sadly to lose his life when the Germans started their big push – he did not get out in time.

I spent six months in Lille in winter 1931-1932 serving an apprenticeship – the only technical training I ever had! In April 1932 I joined the office staff in the M-H office in Ashburton Road, Trafford Park, Manchester. During the depression years and working my way through the office I enrolled as an external student with London University and graduated with a B. Com. in 1937. Then Lionel Harper who was then assistant manager, gave me the opportunity to go out on the road as M-H rep for south-west England. I have nothing but the fondest of memories of Lionel.

It was thus that over the next eight years I learned

Left: Newspaper cutting reporting the early career of Charles Voss.

Below: A shot inside the administration offices of M-H's Barton Dock Road plant in Manchester in 1948. Barton Dock Road was the successor factory to M-H's first assembly plant in nearby Ashburton Road.

MASSEY-HARRIS STAFF AT THE ROYAL SHOW 1939
FRONT ROW—Geo. A. Duke, C. W. Thomas, J. N. Jordan, Managing Director, R. H Guest, J. G. Ritchie.
BACK ROW—Charles & Voss, Mr. Smith of Blackstone & Co., Arthur Cooper, Lionel Harper, Horace Bland, A. Williams.

Left: Representing M-H at the Royal Show in 1939, Charles is first left on the back row.

Below left: At the Royal Agricultural College, Cirencester in 1946 with the King and Queen. Charles Voss behind the M-H

Bottom: The Royal Agricultural College again in 1946 with the M-H 21 Combine and the King and Queen. Charles in centre behind the Combine table.

on the job all about farming and the servicing and operation of farm machinery. My job was considered to be a "reserved occupation" – assembling and servicing farmers in the use of mechanised equipment. We assembled the No. 15 and No. 21 self-propelled combines on the farms and then went back to start off the farmers at harvest time. In a policy of war-time dispersal we also arranged for the assembly of ploughs and binders at selected dealers around the country.

In the Field

I was always keen to get out in the field, helping to assemble and demonstrate the first combines in Italy and Egypt, seeing combines harvesting rice in Mali and Senegal, and sesame in the Sudan. Also seeing mechanised peanut cultivation and the attempts to develop a peanut combine in Senegal and the French Congo. It all later provided me with the experience to

be seconded to the UN FAO in Rome as a consultant in farm mechanisation from 1967-1973. I also had the privilege of travelling with Tom Carroll in Turkey and Iraq – we carried slabs of ice on visits to semi-desert combining operations. He was a great man and a great character.

With this practical M-H background I was able

Right: Charles (2nd from right) at the Paris Salon in 1952 with Portuguese M-H distributors. John Beith, M-H executive on left.

Below: M-F releases Charles for a year to the United Nations to help plan world food supplies.

At the Paris Salon in 1955 with the French made M-H 890 Combine which was based on the Canadian made M-H 90 combine – the biggest of the old style M-H combines. Charles on right, Jan V Meer, the Dutch M-H distributor 2nd from right.

Photo taken in May 1948 after demonstrating the first ever Combine Harvester in Egypt – an M-H 726. Charles on right of front row.

to appreciate, when the merger occurred, how well Ferguson staff were trained in the Ferguson System and complementary equipment. Working for M-H in the UK had been like working for a family business. Everybody knew everybody else and the bosses called us by our first names. After the merger things began to change and we felt, as many Ferguson boys did, that the personal touch had gone and that we were now all part of a bigger and more impersonal whole. I suppose that this is inevitable in a big merger of this kind. I was aware of some of the tension in Engineering and in Sales, but it never affected us in Service.

Production of some implements and the M-H 722 combine had started in Manchester about 1947, before the production of the M-H 726 combine, M-H 701 baler and M-H 744 tractor went into production in Kilmarnock two or three years later. The war had seen big advances in power mechanization in the U.K. and North America. After the war there was a lot of rush for Europe to catch up. This opened up big opportunities, not only in Europe, but also in the Middle East and Africa. Massey-Harris with their factories in Manchester and Kilmarnock were well placed to take advantage of these opportunities.

Demonstrating the M-H 744D tractor in 1949 in Brie Comte Robert in France. Charles to the left.

Four 1949 shots of the first M-H 726 Rice Combine in Italy. Note the rice tracks. Charles alone or on the right of all shots.

The Service Department

In 1951 it became evident to Massey-Harris that sales had to be supported by a Service department. I was posted to Kilmarnock, the source of most of M-H's exports, to set up an Export Service department. The U.K. had its own Service department in Manchester. The function of a service department was to:

a) Provide service cover in the field through our service reps

b) Investigate and report on design, manufacturing and safety problems

c) Train our distributors in the efficient organisation and running of service departments.

We had, at one time, monthly "service" meetings with design engineers and factory inspectors. Many a battle did we have in these meetings. We usually got on well with the factory inspectors. It was helpful for them to know what problems we might be having in the field. But the production people hated to introduce modifications or anything that might affect the daily target throughput of tractors or combines. On one occasion the then director of manufacturing called me into his

One of Charles Voss's Service Notes

private office and threatened to have me sacked if I did not withdraw a report. However, I stood my ground and nothing more was heard. Similar meetings were held at the Marquette and Eschwege factories.

When the merger with Ferguson came about I

Charles was involved with the M-H 701 Baler reconditioning school at the Barton Dock Road plant in 1954. The three shots show delegates from Italy and Denmark.

continued to work for some months out of Kilmarnock. However I was given some additional responsibilities for "indoctrinating" the Ferguson staff in the "red" line of M-H equipment, mainly combines and balers. Initially I used to fly down almost weekly from the old Renfrew airport to Elmdon (now Birmingham International airport) to lecture the Ferguson boys. We in turn, known as the red "Mau Mau" were being indoctrinated with the grey line of tractors and equipment. I found it very stimulating and great fun and we developed an excellent and friendly relationship. After all it was a coming together of the world's greatest combine and tractor manufacturers of the

Charles and team attending to M-H 744D Tractor problems in Oran, Tunisia in 1954.

day.

It was not long before Massey-Harris moved their Export Sales office to the Fletchamstead Highway facility, and my Export Service department likewise moved to this Coventry base. At first I stayed as Export Service department manager for the "red" line, while Maxy Henderson in the next office continued as service manager for the "grey" line. After a short while the distinction between red and grey lines was abolished and Maxy became general service manager for the red and grey lines in the U.K. and I for the export. The assistant Ferguson service manger, Bill

Percival became my assistant, and the M-H service manager for U.K. became Maxy Henderson's assistant.

From the start the relationship between Maxy and myself was excellent. When it came to technical problems, we talked "the same language". We were always able to support each other when it came to making representation on matters of quality to the designers (engineers) and to manufacturing. It was always a pleasure to work with him.

I believe that a similar good relationship was established on the spare parts side. Harry Furminger who at the time of the merger worked in the Ferguson Commercial department in Fletchamstead Highway, in due course became Export Parts manager and went on to become Parts supremo at the Central Parts Operation warehouse in Manchester.

Between 1961 and 1964, Harry Furminger and I organised jointly some eight Parts and Service conferences across Europe, Africa, Latin and Central America. We worked as a team and established a great personal relationship.

Ferguson Impressions
Recalling the Ferguson side-mounted combine I had a bit

Main picture: The first M-F Parts and Service Conference was held at Hedelunde in a former residence of the Kings of Sweden. It was the Training School of A.N.A. Nykoping, the Swedish Ferguson and then M-F distributors.

Left: The first M-F Parts and Service Conference held in Sweden in 1962. Charles is centre, front row.

of field experience with the M-H 21 and M-H 780 combines. So naturally I was interested in what Fergusons were doing. On the M-H side we were always a little sceptical about its potential. But as we look back now, what also happened to the M-H combine production in Kilmarnock Scotland, in Marquette France and Eschwege Germany?

Some Ferguson people were not too impressed by the M-H "top brass" and they considered M-H to be "glorified blacksmiths". There was no doubt some truth in this. The pre-war M-H binders were for many years world leaders. Yet very few, if any, engineering drawings existed in Marquette. Instead they used "patterns" of individual parts. Certainly, the development of sophisticated hydraulic systems, as pioneered by Harry Ferguson, called for more advanced and precise engineering technologies than was present in North America in the farm machinery industry at the time.

Some Ferguson people also seemed to resent the apparent opposition of top M-H people to the LTX tractor. I don't think this can be blamed just on the M-H "top brass". Rather it reflects the big differences in culture between North America and the rest of the world, as exemplified by the enormous differences in farming practices and sizes of holding. Their massive rowcrop acreages of corn, peanuts and cotton have to be taken into account; also that they did not use the tractor for transport anywhere near like as much as do European and farmers of less developed areas – and this still largely holds true today. Most American farmers use trucks for transport and their equipment size is not at all constrained by narrow roads, hedges and gates as in Europe.

The M-H Quarter Century Club – All Brought Together!

M-H had a quarter century club as long I can remember. 25 years service gave one eligibility to join. I qualified in December 1953. All new members received a lapel badge and watch. After the merger the Ferguson boys were duly brought in. The first two members were John Chambers and Alex Patterson.

Within a couple of years it was decided that Banner Lane factory employees – those who had produced the Ferguson tractors under Standard Motor Co. - should be eligible also.

1962 saw Charles involved with the M-F Industrial and Construction Equipment Division, here in Milan, Italy. This M-F 244 Crawler Shovel is an early example of such equipment made in Italy.

In Athens, Greece in 1964 Charles was party to showing off one of M-F's smallest ever Industrial Tractors – an M-F Elf made in Germany. Although classed as a "Leisure Tractor" it was an all yellow machine perhaps aspiring to be classed as an industrial tractor.

Designing all the Way - M-H Kilmarnock to M-F Coventry
(Scotland and England)

Jim Wallace

SPECIAL COURSE No. 9. FERGUSON FOR MASSEY-HARRIS PERSONNEL—25th to 29th JANUARY, 1954.
Back Row, Left to Right—MR. DREWES, MR. J. HALE, MR. HRAB, MR. D. W. McDIARMID (Instructor). MR. EAMES, MR. BUYS, MR. LI. GRIFFITH JONES (Instructor),
MR. W. MOESER, MR. FLOHIMONT.
Front Row, Left to Right—MR. N. PROVEN, MR. B. JOHNSON, MR. BLOOD, MR. MORTON, MR. GRANT.

After the merger M-H personnel had to attend training sessions at the Ferguson Training Centre at Stoneleigh near Coventry. It looks as if the Scotsmen brought their weather down with them!

Jim Wallace joined Massey-Harris in 1950 at their Kilmarnock, Scotland factory. As a design draftsman section leader he saw the design, evolution and modification of many machines in both the M-F and later M-F eras. He worked at Kilmarnock from 1950 to 1960 and then moved, along with many other similar staff, down to Coventry, England. Even to this day the "M-H Scots of Coventry" are a tightly knit group having their regular reunions. Jim in retirement acted as a factory guide at the AGCO MF Banner Lane factory until it closed so over 50 years from signing on, he remained well in touch with the latest designs of MF equipment.

Jim can keep anyone interested in the history of the old M-H made Kilmarnock products (and the men that made them!) entranced for hours, and he has perhaps the best knowledge of employees still alive from this era having been a key player in pulling together the "M-H Scots of Coventry" group.

Jim was responsible for designing many changes to implements. This may seem a somewhat backroom task with little kudos, but it is a crucial support function for the improvement of designs to both prototype and "in production" equipment. Talk to Jim and he will reminisce for hours on so many design changes which farmers have taken for granted over the years. Here I will list but a few.

The combine loading bay at the Kilmarnock factory here seen being used for M-H 726 Combines.

A prototype M-H Fertiliser Spreader.

Massey-Harris 744D Tractor. Jim designed an accelerator lock to ensure that the engine was running at the correct speed for belt work.

Below: A wide front rowcrop version of the M-H 744D Tractor.

Below right: An M-H 744D Tractor stretched to full width in the Kilmarnock factory showroom.

Bottom: A Roadless Half Track Conversion fitted to an M-H 744D Tractor. Few were produced and none are known to have survived.

A rare tricycle rowcop version of the M-H 744D tractor on display at Kilmarnock.

Massey-Harris 703 Baler. There was a problem with chaff and straw pieces accumulating around the knotter causing it to malfunction. Jim designed a blower to run off the main gearbox which blew away the problem. He recalled that the British made M-H 703 baler was not just a direct copy of the North American made No. 3 baler, but had significant design tailoring to better meet British market requirements.

The M-H 703 Baler had knotter problems! This shot is in the yard at the Kilmarnock factory.

One of the engines used to drive the M-H 703 Baler was the Wisconsin twin V air cooled.

Massey-Harris pto adaptions. When the M-H 703 baler was launched, it was vital that it could be driven from the pto of any make of tractor – not just the Massey-Harris tractors of the day. Jim designed the hitch/pto drive variations for the various common tractors of the day.

An M-H 703 Baler with pto drive.

Massey-Harris 712 Manure Spreader. These land drive spreaders were prone to jam in muddy conditions when the wheels gained insufficient traction. The problem was often exacerbated by the advent of tractor manure loaders which resulted in heavy and more compacted loads. The only solution in these circumstances was for the driver to roll up his sleeves and dig out the muck to free the rear beaters. Difficult and messy!

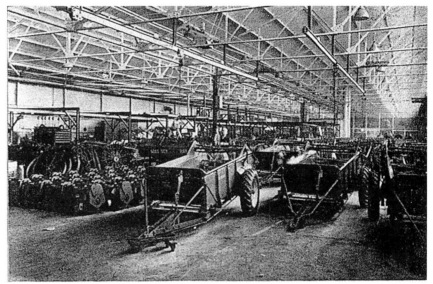

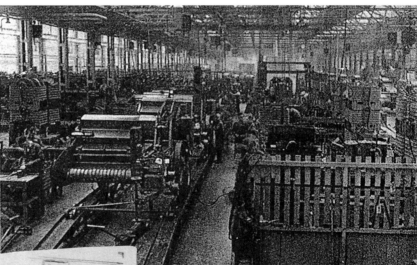

Below: Jim's drawing and prototype of a pto drive for an M-H 712 Manure Spreader.

Making M-H 712 Muck Spreaders (top) and M-H 701 Balers and at Kilmarnock.

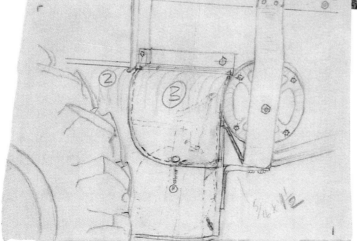

Massey-Harris Drills. There were problems with steel wheel drills in the attachment of spokes to the central hub. Jim fixed it! Keen Massey-Harris machinery enthusiasts can now set themselves the task of identifying the original and modified types of hubs!

Above: Two shots of a prototype M-H Drill which never reached production.

Below and right: Jim modified and showed the M-H Seed Drills.

Prototype Forage Harvester

But Jim was not confined to the drawing office and frequently got out into farm fresh air to help resolve design problems. He was heavily involved in the design and field evaluation of a single prototype trailed pto drive forage harvester. This had a reciprocating blade cutter bar as there was concern at the time that flail type forage harvesters were damaging the sward too much and delaying grass regrowth. He describes it as a very successful machine but at the time Lundell were just doing too well and M-H-F never entered the market with it. In fact the salesmen wanted Lundell machines! Another almost unique feature of the machine was that it had a rubber paddle type auger to take the cut forage up to the chopper. This type of auger created a suction effect which helped to efficiently and evenly deliver the forage to the chopper. The prototype was tested on John Caldwell's fields by the Kilmarnock factory.

Jim also went overseas in the 1970s. One country which is particularly imprinted on his mind is Yugoslavia. He went there to demonstrate the first Canadian combine to be delivered there. It went on to a large state farm as was so typical of the Communist period in Russia and Eastern Europe. Jim was horrified at the large numbers of labourers seen inefficiently hanging around to no purpose in the morning, and who later sloped off after a short day to tend their own small private plots.

Finally, Jim turned up a photo of an M-H 750 combine being sprayed in the Kilmarnock factory. He noted that the workers of the day were issued with a daily milk ration which reputedly prevented lead poisoning.

The prototype M-H Forage Harvester being tested behind a Ferguson tractor at John Caldwell's (see page 76) farm adjacent to the Kilmarnock factory.

Above, below and botom left: Three photos of an M-H 750 trailed Combine fitted out with an M-H Raussendorf Straw Press at the Kilmarnock factory.

Spraying an M-H 750 trailed Combine harvester in the M-H Kilmarnock plant.

The finishing line for
M-H 701 Balers at
Kilmarnock.

"Dogsbody" in Yugoslavia (Yugoslavia)

Bud White

Bud White was a Harry Ferguson employee. He knew nothing of the impending merger and had been demonstrating to Massey-Harris people at Stoneleigh only the day before the merger was announced.

Bud was sent to Yugoslavia in 1956 to help the Yugoslavs set up a Training Centre. It was to have been a six month assignment. He stayed until 1964! When asked what his job title was, he thought a while and then pronounced, "Dogsbody"! Bud had to involve himself with absolutely anything that was required on the day – anything related to training, demonstrations and helping with sales – just keep the job going and

create a good impression with resourceful improvisation whenever required.

The Yugoslavs liked the TE 20 tractors and particularly wanted a good diesel engine version. They were not overly fond of the TEF 20 fitted with the Standard diesel engine because of its poor starting characteristics, but they did like Ferguson engines and Perkins was in the process of establishing licensed production of their P3, P4 and P6 series engines there by IMR. In the event, and prior to the Yugoslavs getting their own Perkins engine production underway, orders were placed with Coventry for TE tractors fitted with Perkins P3 engines. This did not please the Coventry

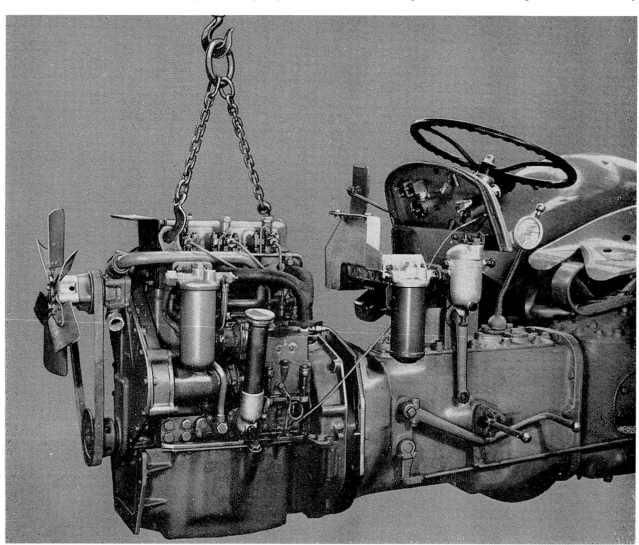

The Perkins P3 diesel engine shown ready for installation.

engineers because they had to design certain structural changes to the basic TE tractor to accommodate the deeper P3 engine.

Initially completely assembled tractors were sent to Yugoslavia with the P3 engines but later, as IMT became established, they were sent out as partial knock down kits. Ultimately the Yugoslavs were to fit their own P3 engines. Bud regarded the P3 engines as a poor engine to service because of their dry liners, connecting rods not identified by weight etc etc.

In 1956 Bud identified potential future orders for 2000 tractors and 15,000 implements. This was met with disbelief in Coventry but it was to transpire. In the event there was a shortage of implements and some "copy" Ferguson implements made in Italy had to be Ferguson badged and supplied. At the time the Massey-Harris factory in Manchester was making some Ferguson implements in line with the new M-H-F policy of making more Ferguson implements in-house, in effect taking work back from Ferguson sub-contractors. The implements being made at Manchester included disc harrows, trailers and mowers.

Bud recalls several quality problems with the Manchester implements including non hardened mower blades and wrong discs on the disc harrows.

Bud operated a lot in the Belgrade to Zagreb area which in geological history had been an old lake of the Danube. Soils were heavy. One task which Bud was assigned was evaluation of a prototype Ferguson mounted beet harvester which M-H-F wanted to sell to Yugoslavia if possible. It was a failure. It would not clean the heavy soils from the beet due to insufficient length of cleaning area inherent in the design of a mounted machines. Wisely, Bud took lots of photographs of how it failed to clean the beet. He prepared his report declaring the machine to be unsuited to Yugoslav conditions and was promptly castigated by his Coventry boss for killing off a good machine! At this Bud produced the photos and his judgement was grudgingly accepted.

Ferguson equipment that was popular in Yugoslavia included mowers, disc harrows and tillers. The disc harrows were not heavy enough for heavier soils unless it had been ploughed in the autumn and a frost tilth established. Massey-Harris maize planters and steerage hoe cultivators were also imported from M-H-F South Africa. The high lift loader on the M-H-F and M-F 35 tractors was also well received.

Reflecting on the merger, Bud thinks that quite a few Ferguson principles were betrayed most importantly including the Ferguson spanner of renown "one fits all" principle. However he is quick to acknowledge how Massey-Harris widened Ferguson's scope and appeal with its combines and balers.

And finally, an overview of how MF in the UK progressed in the decade after Massey-Harris-Ferguson

The final contributor has deliberately been taken out of the alphabetical order of all those above because I felt that it gives an impression of how Massey-Ferguson moved on.

Onwards from M-H-F. Massey-Ferguson 1960-1970. Reorganisation, Problems, Development

Lance Parker hails from a Massey-Harris dealer background, his company having lost the franchise as a result of the merger. He subsequently, much to his own surprise, moved back to the Massey fold where he held the post of Marketing Director. As such he has been able to provide a unique overview of happenings in the company in the decade after the merger.

"At the time of my joining Massey-Ferguson in June 1960 with the background of being a Director of a large Ford Dealership with car, truck and tractor franchises, I wondered what I had let myself in for!

The business was disorganised, with a low level of employee morale, an ailing product line and a disillusioned distributor network. The Corporation appointed the McKinsey Group to advise on how to place the U.K. company in a viable unit within the M-F world-wide group of companies.

Four Directors, including the Managing Director,

Early days with M-H. Lance Parker (centre) discusses the merits of the M-H 712 Manure Spreader with M-H President James Duncan (left end of spreader). Hilldenborough, Kent.

Larry Pomeroy and wife (centre) with L. T. Ritchie, Vice-President and Managing Director of the Australian companies and wife; Dick Muspratt (see page 207) to right hosting them in Australia.

had resigned. It was necessary to recruit new executives to deal with the problems confronting the Corporation within the UK company. The President of the Corporation, Albert Thornbrough, had a clear vision of what was required to put things right in the U.K. In February 1960 through John Shiner, Corporate Vice-President Marketing, the transfer from Australia to the U.K. of Lawrence H. Pomeroy, an American, was arranged. Mr Pomeroy had carried out a similar operation of reorganising the Australian Company. He took up the position of Marketing Director. He and his wife worked as a team in bringing together a group of people, some from overseas, to form an effective Marketing Organisation in the UK. As Marketing Director UK his designated priorities were to:

- Establish a contemporary and competitive company marketing organization at head office and in the field

- Identify a British replacement as Director of Marketing, M-F, UK

- Initiate the integration of the M-H and Ferguson Distributor/Dealer operations and establish a vigorous M-F Distributor/Dealer network

- Strive for market leadership in key product areas.

Later in the year the appointment of Gilbert A. Hunt as Managing Director took place, his skills being connected with Manufacturing. He was an excellent "front man" in Industry affairs, becoming President of the Agricultural Engineers Association within a few months of joining the Company. He also played an important role in moulding all levels of the management team together, creating a feeling of pride and stability within the UK operation.

This action by top management was a successful move and Larry Pomeroy made a significant contribution to the fortunes of the Company over the ensuing two years. He was a great leader and drew

up a list of priorities to be pursued in the efforts to reinstate MF as the market leader in the manufacturing and distribution of farm equipment in the UK. The order of priorities was as detailed below and moved forward in conjunction with Marketing staff and Field Sales Management:

1. To rationalise the number of distribution outlets in the UK and reinstate the distributors' confidence in MF.

The situation was that insufficient attention had been given at the time of the merger to eliminate inter franchise trading conflict created by having too many distributors/dealers. Some products were still being manufactured in two colours, red for sale to the previous M-H dealers and grey for the previous Ferguson distributors.

The attitude of employees was also noticeable, some still tainted with grey and some with red, illustrating that full integration of the companies had not taken place. It was important to deal with this situation quickly to ensure survival and profitability of those distributors/dealers to be retained.

We had a good idea of the number and location of the retail outlets required to give a satisfactory level of service to the user, based on the principle that he should not have to travel more than 30/40 miles to the nearest outlet. To confirm this, we studied a Land Utilisation Map of the UK to identify the desired locations to serve the farmers. By using a clear plastic overlay with red pins inserted to illustrate the desired location, according to the map, with another overlay using green pins showing the existing arrangements. We were then able to select the dealers within the area who had potential for future development to be retained. It was planned to reduce the number of outlets from 510 to 230, owned and controlled by 190 Dealer Principals. The objective was to have fewer and better quality distributors to sell and service MF's products.

The implementation of this was exacerbated by a situation where we had one large distributor representing us in a territory covering some 12% of the landmass and purchases from the Company amounting to 15% of the UK market turnover. Due to infringments of the terms and conditions within the Distributor agreement it became necessary for the termination of their agreement. To find alternative distribution outlets in such a large area was a mammoth task. The requirement was to

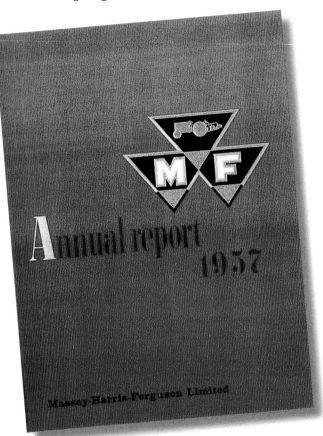

The last M-H-F Annual Report, but bearing that famous M-F three triangle logo.

appoint nine Distributor Principals with a total of thirteen locations which took two years!

Progress was being made in other parts of the country and the rationalisation of distribution took three years to complete. The operation proved to be an overall success, the prime criteria for measuring the effectiveness of the action taken being the market share statistics relating to tractor registrations in the UK. In the early sixties MF market share had declined from around 37% to 28.5% and it climbed back to 41% by the late sixties.

In the meantime Larry Pomeroy had made great progress in introducing the marketing concept into the UK operations and morale throughout the company and the distribution organisation was improving, everyone seemed to be enthusiastic about carrying out their responsibilities. The appointment of eight General Managers within Marketing had taken place to control the functions of:-

Sales, Service, Business Management (a confidential department exclusively for dealers), Market Research, General Administration, Product Planning, Product Training and Distribution Development.

In February 1961 Mr Peter J Wright was appointed as General Sales Manager. He was previously with Ford. He proved to be a great asset to the business and on Larry Pomeroy's return to North America in 1962 he became UK Marketing Director at which time I was appointed to the position of General Sales Manager.

In early 1960 the UK was split into three regions, Southern, Central and Northern, under the control of Regional Managers, reporting to the General Sales Manager, with a field force of Area Managers reporting to them. The Regional Managers had full authority to make decisions in response to distributors/dealers' queries, providing they were in line with the laid down company policy. This management structure was introduced to improve communications and the relationship between the company and its distributor/dealer principals. The intention was to create a better understanding with the principals, of the aims and objectives of the company, in its plans to regain market leadership in the farm machinery industry in the UK.

It was important for the company to have a profitable distributor network, hence the establishment of the Business Management function as a strictly confidential department, with no access to the figures by MF without the Distributor Principals' permission.

Many public relation functions together with sales promotion programmes were introduced to create a high level of enthusiasm amongst the distributor principals and their staff, particularly their salesmen. This prompted our chief competitor to display notices on our trade stand at the Royal Show saying "Omo Washes Whiter", this was taken as a compliment to the effectiveness of the programmes!

An interesting morale booster and successful programme was a presentation in September 1961, based on the story of mechanised farming from the days of the Roman Legions in Britain until today. It was carried out by professional actors assisted by personnel from the Product Training Centre at Stoneleigh and took place at the vast grounds of the Training School. It was a story of the men and machines setting the pace for posterity in the all-important realms of farming and titled "The Pageant of the Pacesetters" with choreography by professionals.

The presentation was performed every evening for a period of one week with the assistance of professionally programmed lighting effects including spotlights and searchlights. Each show was devoted to a specific audience including Staff and Workers from the various factories operated by the company, major shareholders, banks, finance houses, corporate management, UK and export dealer principals and their senior staff, selected suppliers and all personnel employed by the company. The finale of the presentation was a parade and massive display of all the products available within the MF franchise, a most convincing array, some three hundred machines.

Much of the success achieved by this programme must be accredited to Captain D C Hill, DSO, RN, ret'd., who was General Manager and Principal of the Product Training Centre at the time. The event was supported by music being played by the Band of the Royal Marines, Duncan Hill's choice and favourite.

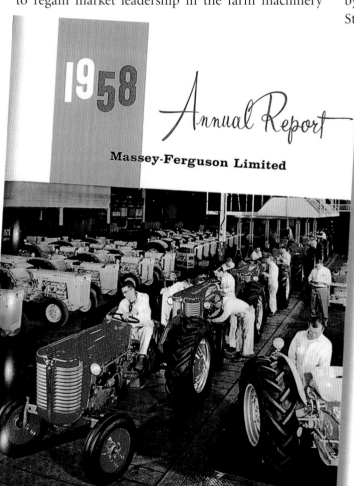

The first M-F Annual Report.

A 1994 line-up of M-F Service personnel and their vehicles at the Stoneleigh Training Centre. Captain Hill had an early influence on the development of the Centre in Ferguson times.

It was felt that it was necessary to create a more friendly relationship between all levels of company management and distributor principals and their senior staff by arranging an annual social function where everyone could gather in a convivial atmosphere. This was achieved by the introduction of a "Ladies Night" festival and a ball supported by a top grade cabaret and was held every December, during Smithfield Show week, at the London Hilton where around six hundred guests were entertained.

It was also helpful that the Royal Show had been centred at Stoneleigh as a permanent site for this annual event, as opposed to the changing venue each year. Naturally MF had brought some influence to bear on the Royal Agricultural Society of England in reaching their decision to locate the Show at Stoneleigh, adjoining the company's Product Training Centre.

It is difficult to say that the distribution rationalisation programme had been completed because, unlike products it is a living thing, subject to changes brought about by family matters. A satisfactory situation was in being by the mid-sixties, with a progressive increase in market penetration, reinforced by the introduction of the new range of tractors in 1964 when the 135, 165 and 175 came into being and the importation of the 1100 series from North America commenced. This development was a significant change in the policy and philosophy of the company in moving into the growth market of the heavier and higher horsepower units.

This brings us to another item in the list of priorities drawn up by Larry Pomeroy:-

2. The upgrading of the product line with special emphasis being given to tractors and combine harvesters.

The range of products being marketed by the company in 1960 consisted of the following:-

The MF 35 and 65 tractors manufactured at Banner Lane, Coventry.

The 788 Combine Harvester manufactured at the Kilmarnock Factory. The French built 892 Combine was being imported, in the short term, to provide a higher capacity model until the 400/500 machines became available.

A whole range of general machines including seed drills, mowers, tillage equipment, potato planter, potato harvester, manure spreaders etc., was being manufactured at Trafford Park, Manchester. The factory also manufactured a range of industrial equipment including tractor digger loaders, excavators, dump trucks and trailers.

Rubery Owen continued to supply a range of equipment to suit the Ferguson System.

Tractors

As noted the declining share of the tractor market was a concern. This was partially due to the distribution problems as already stated, but the prime cause was the performance of the tractors.

The MF 35 was the first red and grey tractor to be manufactured by the company since the merger. It was fitted with the Standard Motor Co.'s 23C diesel engine; this was an indirect fuel injection engine and proved to be difficult to start. This demanded that drastic action needed to be taken, if the declining market penetration was to be arrested.

A crash programme was introduced to replace the Standard Motor's 23C engine by fitting the Perkins A3152 engine, a 3 cylinder direct fuel injection unit having better torque characteristics for agricultural applications. The tractor was again later re-launched as the 35X and proved to have a good market acceptance.

Full integration. M-H 735 Combine and M-H designed M-F 703 Baler with Ferguson design M-F 35 Tractor.

Massey-Ferguson
in the
United Kingdom

Unfortunately it left a problem of disposing of a vast quantity of early MF 35 tractors held in inventory, with a high cost liquidation programme.

A similar problem existed with the 65 tractor equipped with the Perkins AD4.192 engine which was also an indirect fuel injection engine and experienced the same bad starting characteristics as the MF 35. This was overcome by fitting the Perkins AD4.203 unit, which had direct fuel injection. Fortunately no liquidation of tractors in inventory was required, as stocks were very low.

At the time of the launch of the new range of 100 series tractors (international coding DX series) in 1964 the 135 tractor was equipped with the Perkins 3A152 engine, the 165 with the Perkins AD4.203 and the 178 had the 4A.248. We were now in the growth market of the heavy, higher horsepower tractors and enjoying good market penetration. The "jewel in the crown" was to obtain the approval for the manufacturing source of the heavy tractor to be in the UK. Although excavation for the installation of an assembly track had commenced at Banner Lane, corporate management decided ultimately that this tractor be manufactured in France.

The market acceptance of the new range of

Lance Parker showing H.M. the Queen M-F exhibits at the Royal Smithfield Show where the MF 100 series Tractors were launched. Albert Thornbrough, the President of M-F is to the left of the Queen. Her Majesty apparently asked, "Why were the MF 100 series tractors so unique?" to which Lance Parker replied "ergonomic factors including a cigarette lighter!"

Lance Parker (right) discussing the merits of the M-F 165 tractor with Albert Thornbrough, the first President of M-F.

tractors with increased market share created a lot of confidence within the distribution organisation. It was, however, difficult to sustain as our chief competitor Ford had also launched a new range of tractors providing formidable competition. In such circumstances and in hindsight, it was fortuitous that action had already been taken to strengthen our distributor/dealer network in the rationalisation programme. This enabled them to fight direct competition as opposed to destroying each other with inter franchise competition.

Combine Harvesters – MF 400s and 500s

The M-F Smithfield Show, London in probably 1962 or 1963 as would be evidenced by the exhibiting of the USA made M-F Super 90 Tractor.

Harry Ferguson's Detroit Tractor Plant was expanded by 100% in 1958. Note the industrial adaptations of the Ferguson TO 35 tractors, and the plant still badged as Massey-Harris-Ferguson.

Massey-Harris had for many years been one of the world leaders in combine harvester development and sales. It was in the late 1950s that things began to change, the more particularly so in Europe. Intense competition from Claas in Germany and Claeyson in Belgium began to erode the market share enjoyed by MF, to the extent that in the UK, their share of market had fallen from around 70% in the late 50s to 32% in 1962.

The main design feature creating this situation was the width of the threshing drum. The Massey Harris design, or call it the North American requirement, was for harvesting crops with a low straw to grain ratio, where straw rarely grew to more than 30 inches

high. In Australia it was 12-18 in.

In Europe the requirement was for handling crops with a very high straw to grain ratio. In the UK the average length of straw was 5-6 ft; in the Polder Dam area in Holland where most of our testing was carried out, it could be up to 7 ft tall. The MF 788 had a threshing drum width of 32 in. restricting the output of the machine to a capacity well below the machines being imported from the Continent which were equipped with 30-50 in. drums.

Fortunately, we already had prototype machines being tested in the field which were successfully launched in September 1961 in preparation for the 1962 harvest. The dealers responded well to the launch of the machines known as the MF 400, a 37 in. drum machine, and the MF 500 had a 45 in. drum. Orders were taken with full payment on the day of the launch for 507 of the 400 machines and 646 of the 500s – a grand total off 1153 and not one single production machine had been produced!

Although such a response to the launch was

Lance Parker discusses the new M-F 400/500 series combines with H.M. the Queen Mother at a Royal Smithfield Show.

magnificent in itself, it created a major problem for the company at the Kilmarnock factory in negotiating new piece rates with the workers on the shop floor. Production of the machines was scheduled to commence at Kilmarnock at the beginning of October but did not start until December 18th.

In the meantime the dealers had gone out and sold the machines they had paid for and in many cases had also disposed of the second-hand combines they had taken in part exchange. Production on the single line track commenced with the 500 machine, with an initial daily output of 4/6 machines, optimising at 18 per day at the end of March, at which time we had produced sufficient of the 500 machines to meet the orders taken. From these production figures it became evident that the total requirement of 1153 units would not be met in time for the rapidly approaching harvest season.

The Company therefore faced a crisis unless it could produce sufficient machines to enable distributors to meet their commitment to the customers who had ordered the 400 machine and in most cases paid for them. It was Peter Wright's idea to continue producing the model 500 to meet the 507 orders taken for the 400 machine and ask the distributors to re-negotiate the deal with every farmer who had ordered a 400 machine to change to a 500. Not an easy task, it also placed the farmer in a very strong bargaining position. This arrangement was a very expensive way of dealing with the problem, the only other alternative was for the Company not to meet its commitment to supply the machines and this would have been disastrous.

Unfortunately, immediately prior to the implementation of the scheme, in March 1962, Peter became seriously ill due to a "bug" he had picked up during his world-wide travels and was unable to return to his job until December. I was appointed to the office of Acting Director Marketing. On his return he made great progress and in June 1964 he took up the position of Corporate Vice-President Marketing to replace John Shiner, who I regret to say had resigned from the Corporation. John was a wise counsellor to have around, a man of integrity with marketing skills.

The budgeted cost of the programme to convert the

The M-F 35 and 65 Tractor era at a Smithfield Show, London in probably the late 1950s. Note that the new style M-F 400/500 Combine is present along with an old style M-F 788 Combine.

orders from the 400 machines to the 500 was £591,000 which needed to have corporate approval and was readily given, thus putting another nail in the unions' "coffin" in the minds of corporate management. In the event the newly established distributor organisation was successful in converting every order at a total cost of £312,000, such was the understanding and mutual trust which had been cultivated between the company and the distributor principals in a very short period of time. We all breathed a sigh of relief, thinking our problems were all over. Unfortunately this was not to be so, as we were accused by the Machinery Committee of the National Farmers Union (NFU) of being unfair to the farmers who had purchased the 500 machine and demanded that we compensate them accordingly.

We were invited to Agricultural House, Knightsbridge in London to attend a meeting of the President and county Chairmen of the NFU. The purpose was for us to give an explanation of the action we had taken in supplying the larger machines to those farmers who had ordered the smaller machines at more favourable terms than farmers who had ordered the large machines. After much contentious argument and discussion, the reasons we gave were accepted and we were complimented for the action we had taken in meeting our commitment to those farmers who had ordered the 400 machine.

Combine Harvester Strategy

In 1968 UK Marketing were instructed by corporate management to develop a combine harvester strategy for Europe, a most interesting and fascinating challenge. It took ten months to prepare and was presented to the President and corporate management at a two day meeting in Coventry in early 1969, supported by a Financial Analysis illustrating the viability of the project. The strategy was based upon there being three sizes of machines, small, medium and large with all the variables required according to the territories and conditions in which they would be operated.

The important issue for the

UK company was the manufacturing source of each of the machines; UK Marketing recommended the following:-

Small machine: Germany.
Medium machine: France.
Large machine: UK (Kilmarnock).

The President thanked Marketing for the presentation and adjourned the meeting for two hours for the purpose of his Vice-Presidents to consider the proposals.

The meeting was reconvened at 5 p.m. and he complimented the UK Company on all technical aspects of the Product line Strategy, stating that it would be adopted and instructed the various Engineering Functions to proceed with all possible speed. The target date for prototype machine availability was to be January 1971. He however condemned the sources of manufacturing recommended by UK Marketing to be totally irresponsible, the more especially so in view of our experience with the trade unions with the 400 and 500 machines in 1961/2. The President announced that the sources of manufacture would be:-

Small machine: Germany.
Medium machine: UK.
Large machine: France.

No further discussion took place and the meeting was closed. It was a great disappointment to the UK Company not to be granted the manufacture of the high volume and profitable large capacity machine.

That famous logo and a Ferguson dominated M-F line up of equipment in 1957.

General Machines

Many changes in type and application took place with mowers and other machines over the years. MF kept their place in the market with the general run of machines but it was never able to compete with Ransome, Simms and Jefferies (RS&J) in the tillage range of equipment, particularly ploughs. There appeared to be two alternatives, the first being to negotiate a deal with RS&J to supply us, or perhaps to buy them out, the second being to develop a completely new range of ploughs utilising our own resources. The former was unfortunately a non-runner due to the supply agreement and strong relationship with our chief competitor for it appeared that whatever we offered to purchase RS&J, Ford would outbid us. We searched Europe for a supplier without success and received corporate management approval to proceed with our own development programme with a capital expenditure limit of Canadian $ 5 million (3 C$ to £1 at that time).

It was at about this time that we were approached by I.C.I. (Dr. Boon) to inform us that in their opinion and according to their research programmes, the days of the plough were numbered. They claimed that in the future, chemical farming would replace the traditional and conventional methods of cultivating the soil by the use of their newly discovered chemical, Paraquat. The process would be known as minimum tillage, involving the spraying machine being used immediately after the harvest had been gathered. Experiments had been carried on a limited scale in different parts of the country having varying soil conditions, for example in Wiltshire, with well-drained light chalky land as opposed to, say, Lincolnshire and Essex with their heavy wet and cold clay conditions.

The major problem in heavy soil conditions was to obtain penetration of the rolling disc which made a slit in the soil in which the seed was to be sown and Dr Boon wanted to know whether we could help in resolving the problem. It so happened that with our advanced hydraulics we had recently launched Pressure Control. We had always had Depth control as

Early Massey-Ferguson at the Royal Show. Note still the M-H style Combine and Ferguson style MF 35 and 65 Tractors.

The M-F 130 Direct Drill designed for minimum tillage.

a feature of the Ferguson system but pressure control added new dimensions to our unique hydraulics.

In this case Pressure Control would enable a downward pressure to be applied to the seed drill, thus assisting the rolling discs to penetrate heavy soil. Unfortunately, the seed drills on the market at that time had insufficient strength to withstand the downward pressure required to achieve the desired penetration. Dr. Boon asked whether it would be possible for us to design a 30 row combined seed and fertilizer drill to suit the purpose. At this point we felt that we should consult with Corporate Product Planning to not only discuss the project but also to consider the implications involved in the development of the new range of ploughs.

The matter was referred to the President who stated that we should work alongside I.C.I. with their field test programmes and design the drill, provided that a price could be agreed. He also emphasised that extreme caution should be exercised in getting too involved as he was of the opinion that progressive toxicity of the soil in future years could occur with repeated applications of Paraquat.

It was agreed with I.C.I. to design and manufacture the drills at a price of £12,500 each and they placed an order for twelve machines. Field test programmes commenced and although comparative crop yields with the conventional method of sowing were fairly satisfactory on lighter soils, the yield on heavy soil conditions was depressed mainly due to the seed not germinating, particularly with winter sown crops in wet cold clay.

The process of sowing with "minimum tillage" was, after spraying the stubble with Paraquat and leaving the chemical for sufficient time to kill off the weed infestation, say 4-5 days, the seed drill could then be put to work. The rolling discs penetrated the soil to the desired depth to make a slit, followed by small shoes to open a furrow, immediately behind which followed the seed tubes, dropping the seed and fertilizer into the furrows and small shoes following the tubes to close the slit. At the time of my leaving the Company in August 1969, little progress had been made in the development or procurement of a suitable manufacturer to compete with the range of ploughs marketed by RS&J who dominated the market for tillage equipment.

The basic range of general farm machines changed very little over the years, except for items such as mowers where innovations like the flail type forage harvester and rotary mowers had changed the practice of grassland farming. Making hay was considered to be the salvation of grass whereas the making of silage was considered to be the conservation of grasses.

Distributor Profits; Integrated Planning and

MEMORIES

MHF

Control

The action taken in all the aspects mentioned here rendered the M-F "Full product line Franchise" as a most attractive and profitable business operation in the distribution of farm machinery in the UK. The objective was to make it possible for our distributors to show at least 20% return on their capital invested in the sales and servicing of M-F equipment.

At the time I left the Company a satisfactory return on capital was being achieved by many of our aggressive and efficient distributors. Shortly after joining the company in 1960, Mr Pomeroy asked me what sort of return would be acceptable to the distributors of our products in the UK, when I responded by expressing a figure of 20% was achievable, or they might as well put the money in a Building Society account. He then referred to a file of correspondence with the Distributor Association Council and the previous company Management, where a figure

of 7.5% was stated as the best that could be expected in the industry.

The management tool of Integrated Planning and Control was introduced and every manager was expected to develop an Action Programme to rectify problems connected with his area of responsibilities. As an example each Action Programme would be developed, according to the subject, something like the following:

"Autumn Gold"

1. The Objective e.g. Increase tractor penetration from 32% to 40%.
2. The Strategy to be employed e.g. introduce sales promotion scheme which provides incentive direct to Distributor Salesmen in the form of awarding fabulous holidays to salesmen achieving highest performance over target etc.
3. The Method e.g. develop programme with Sales

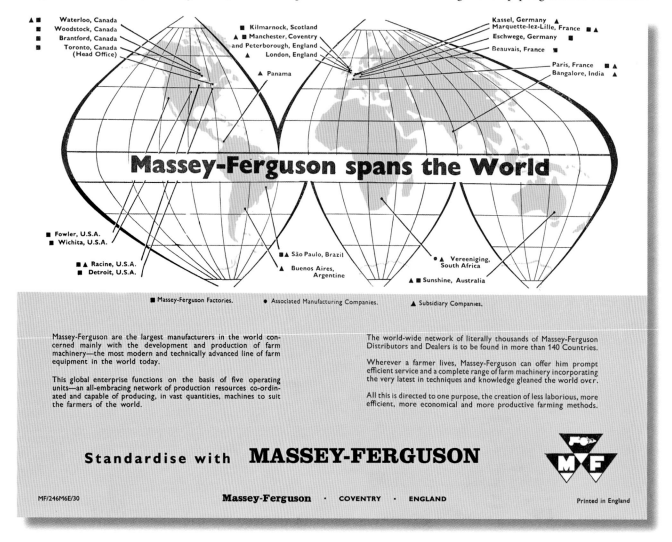

From the rear cover of an early M-F brochure showing the extent of M-F's world-wide operations.

Promotion and Advertising Agency.

4. Timing e.g. over period of three months, 1st September-30th November.

5. Responsibility. General Sales Manager and Field Staff etc.

6. Profit impact including the cost of the programme

The above example serves as an illustration of Action Programmes, which would be submitted by each function of the Company, i.e. Marketing, Finance, Manufacturing, Engineering Planning and Procurement, and Personnel and Industrial Relations. Each of these functions was headed up by a director of the Company, reporting to the Managing Director and where appropriate the Corporate Vice-President responsible for each of the activities.

The purpose of reporting to the Corporate Vice-

Presidents was to seek advice on the matter, not to obtain approval. Having received the advice, it was the functional head's decision whether to accept the advice or back his own judgement, as it was important for the management of the Company to be seen as being controlled from Coventry rather than Toronto. Mark you if you decided to go your own way you had better be sure you were doing the right thing!

Integrated Planning and Control operated throughout the Organisation and in my opinion was an excellent management tool in controlling the business. A Co-ordinating Committee Meeting was held each month to review the various functions' activities and performance with decisions being made to deal with the problems that had arisen. There is of course much more that could be said about running such a complex business as Massey Ferguson, with

The re-builder of M-H-F and creator of Massey-Ferguson, Albert Thornbrough seen at the windows of the company's headquarters in 1958. The building was built in 1879. Thornbrough is credited with restoring the company's dried up liquidity when he inherited it in July 1956 with a gigantic inventory of un-sold machines. (source: Fortune October 1958).

Visiting Sir Winston Churchill. Lionel Harper (MD of M-H in UK to left of Sir Winston, Christopher Soames in short jacket, Lance Parker to right of Soames, brother R Parker to right of Lance and farm manager Mr Cox behind Sir Winston.

its wide range of products, with varying seasonal requirements throughout the world. Who wants to buy a combine harvester or a baler in December apart from some third world country where their summer occurs during our winter and they haven't the money to do so! And so on, but the factories have to continue producing throughout the year.

A Miracle for Winston Churchill

Perhaps a little light digression before I end might not go amiss, it concerns an experience I had prior to joining M-F. We were M-H dealers at the time. My Company was approached by Massey-Harris in January 1952 to seek our opinion as to whether Winston Churchill, who farmed about 300 acres at Chartwell in Kent, would accept as a gift a combine harvester and a baler. They wanted to present the machines as a token of their appreciation for the magnificent contribution he had made in the defeat of Germany during the Second World War.

We undertook to discuss the matter with him, his reaction was to accept the most generous offer, on the strict understanding and confirmed in writing, that the arrangement would not have any effect on the UK Treasury. It must be a gift from Massey-Harris Canada with the approval of the Canadian Government. These conditions were duly accepted and the machines were

delivered to Chartwell in time for the 1952 harvest, the combine was a model 222 built in Canada and the baler was a 701 built at the Manchester factory.

The arrival of the machines at Chartwell caused quite a stir with the local inhabitants, as the sight of a combine harvester was something unusual in those days. We put the machines to work. Mr Churchill was excited and thrilled to see the combine in operation on a badly laid crop of barley and to everyone's alarm insisted on driving the machine. He was Prime Minister at the time and so there was much concern about his safety but his bodyguard, Detective Inspector Thompson, said it would be impossible to change his mind if he was set on doing it. He had retained the services of an ex-prisoner of war named Hans as his farm foreman, whom he wanted to accompany him on the platform of the machine when he was driving it. He drove it round the field twice, quite successfully and as he dismounted from the machine he said, "it's a miracle" and that is my view of such a sophisticated piece of machinery.

Final Reflections

When I left M-F it was a strong and vibrant unit

Lance Parker's most treasured photo – Sir Winston and Lady Churchill.

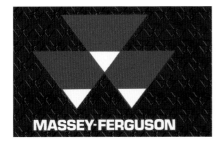

and the profits were contributing a not insignificant sum to the global M-F business. The British unit was well respected by other M-F units around the world although they were sympathetic about the problems we experienced with Trade Unions. Morale was high with all the staff and strong mutual trust had been established with the distributors. Massey-Ferguson was a "Happy Ship". Whilst the foregoing may have given an impression of being anti the

trade unions, nothing could be further from the truth. I always believed that they were an essential part of management, but there is no place for the militant style leadership that we had to encounter at Kilmarnock and Coventry.

My almost 10 years with M-F were without reservation the happiest of my whole career.

1958. One of the first M-F landmarks in North America as top brass celebrate the 1,200,000th tractor to come out of what had been Harry Ferguson's tractor plant at Detroit.

OTHER BOOKS BY JOHN FARNWORTH
AVAILABLE FROM JAPONICA PRESS

The Massey Legacy

This two-volume set contains a wealth of information on Massey products, including tractors, general farm equipment, harvesting machinery, industrial, landscape, household and forestry equipment, stationary engines, memorabilia, Massey Harris in wartime, serial numbers, model and engine data.

Vol. 1 401 pages, approx. 700 illustrations, Hardback, *£29.95*. ISBN 1 904 686 04 4

Vol. 2 372 pages, approx. 600 illustrations, Hardback, *£29.95*. ISBN 0 9540222 8 9

Fergusons: The Hunday Experience.

Written in conjunction with John Moffitt, this huge volume presents a great deal of information about Ferguson history which has evolved out of the creation and presentation of his unique private collection of Ferguson equipment, literature and memorabilia. A beautifully designed book which all Ferguson enthusiasts will want to own.

400 pages, 700 illustrations, Hardback, *£29.95*. ISBN 0 9533737 5 4

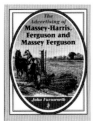

The Advertising of Massey-Harris, Ferguson and Massey Ferguson

A remarkable and evocative collection of advertising material charting 150 years of tractor and agricultural machinery progress, this book will be of value to all those interested in the history of tractors and agricultural machinery, and also advertising and literature enthusiasts.

320 pages, 342 illustrations, mainly colour. Hardback, *£19.95*. ISBN 0 9540222 7 0

A Worldwide Guide to Massey Harris, Ferguson & Early Massey Ferguson Tractors.

Concisely brings together and defines the extensive tractor family of some 300 models which preceded the Massey Ferguson 100 series tractors launched in 1964. Presents concise and basic specifications for each model of tractor together with photographs of representative model types. The tractors are grouped in chapters according to their country of manufacture, with the specifications preceding the photographs.

248 pages, well illustrated. Hardback, *£27.95*. ISBN 0 9533737 6 2

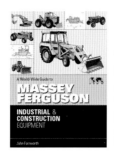

A World -Wide Guide to Massey Ferguson Industrial and Construction Equipment

This book identifies an incredible 26 basic types of industrial equipment which were produced and marketed by MF. It was prepared as a result of extensive research over three years, involving contact with specialists in UK, America, Europe, Australia, South Africa and Brazil. It provides a valuable reference text and identification guide for industrial equipment enthusiasts, all those interested in the general history of Massey Ferguson and most especially the growing band of Massey Ferguson Industrial equipment collectors world wide.

320 pages. Extensive Illustrations, Hardback
£29.95. ISBN 0 9540222 0 3

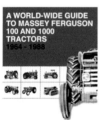

A World-Wide Guide to Massey Ferguson 100 and 1000 tractors 1964-1988

The 100 and 1000 series consists of a range of tractors from about 20-200 hp with all types of chassis combinations – 2 WD, 4 WD, crawlers and articulated. Using Massey Ferguson archive material collected from around the world, John has carefully identified some 250 models and variants, and described each type with specifications and photographs.

John Farnworth

310 pages. Extensive Illustrations. Hardback,
£29.95. ISBN 1 904686 05 2

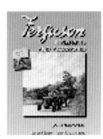

Ferguson Implements and Accessories

The first comprehensive book to be produced on this subject, this book focuses mainly on the wide equipment range produced for the British-made Ferguson TE tractors, but also includes equipment made in the United States for Ford Ferguson and Ferguson TO tractors. There is reference to implements made for the South Africa market, and a colour section reproduces present-day advertising material from India, where Ferguson style implements are still manufactured. The text includes basic technical details of the equipment. This revised edition has a new section featuring over 50 more products.

220 pages, very well illustrated mainly in black & white. Hardback
£18.50 ISBN No. 978-1-904686-08-8.